The JOURNEY HOME

A NOVEL

YECHIEL ECKSTEIN

SHAVTI HOUSE

Published in Chicago, Illinois, by Shavti House 3844 Enfield, Skokie, IL 60076.

Jacket design by Richmond & Williams.
Book design by BookSetters.

Old Testament quotations are from *The TANAKH: The New JPS Translations according to the Traditional Hebrew Text*. Copyright © 1985 by the Jewish Publication Society. Used by permission.

New Testament quotations are from *The New Revised Standard Version of the Bible*, copyright © 1989 by the Division of Christian Education of the National Council of the Churches of Christ in the USA. Used by permission. All rights reserved.

Library of Congress Control Number: 2001087320
ISBN 0-9708188-0-7

Printed in the United States of America
1 2 3 4 5 6 7 — 06 05 04 03 02 01

DEDICATION

To my children—
Tamar
Talia & Jeff
Yael
—who bring much joy, challenge, fulfillment,
and meaning to my life.

VESHAVTI bevait Hashem leorech yamim.
And I shall dwell in the house of the LORD forever.
—PSALM 23:6

Ki yesh tikvah leachareetecha . . .
VESHAVU vanim leegvulam.
And there is hope for your future . . .
Your children shall return to their country.
—JEREMIAH 31:17

The Hebrew word *shavti* has a twofold meaning of "I dwelled" and "I returned." Its most compelling articulation is perhaps found in the biblical verses above. Shavti House Press is committed to the publication of those works expressing this dual connotation of spiritual journey and "arrival," both to the presence of God as well as to one's spiritual center.

INTRODUCTION

This book, although technically fiction, has its seeds in actual events and a real friendship I had with Evangelical Christian pastor Jamie Buckingham. Jamie loved Israel, especially its mountains and desert, and visited it frequently. He also had a warm heart for the Jewish people and their faith.

We often dreamed about hiking up Mount Sinai and, hand in hand, receiving God's holy word—he as a Christian, I as a Jew. This dream showed the love we shared for one another and the spiritual nourishment we drew from each other's religious traditions.

Unfortunately, this dream was not to be. Jamie died February 1992 at the still tender age of fifty-nine.

But Jamie's passing sparked a wonderful development, the beginning of another friendship I cherish deeply to this day. I met John French, one of Jamie's best friends, at Jamie's memorial service, and John has since been a source of wisdom, encouragement, and inspiration to me .

Jamie's death also inspired the idea for this book. At a speech I gave to the Community of Jesus in Cape Cod,

Massachusetts, which Jamie had frequented, the much respected Christian writer David Manuel approached me when I had finished my remarks. He said that "God spoke to his heart" with the idea that I tell my "bridge-building" story through the metaphorical trek up Mount Sinai that Jamie and I never got to actually take. Not only would this honor Jamie's memory, but it could also inspire other Christians and Jews to stretch out their hands to one another in dialogue, respect, and love, greatly enriching their lives of faith. With those goals in mind, I devoted myself to writing this book.

Underlying my world-view and religious beliefs is the notion that God is God of the world, not just of our particular group or denomination, though some of us seem to forget this from time to time. He calls out for us to know Him and to know ourselves, and to embark on a spiritual pilgrimage toward the actualization of our spiritual identities and the fulfillment of our existential selves.

I believe deeply that God is bidding Christians and Jews to walk up Mount Sinai down separate yet parallel paths. Like Martin Buber, who captured this idea so magnificently in his I-thou concept, I believe the Jew can reach fulfillment *as a Jew* when he encounters his fellow man, the other, in the presence of the Ultimate Other, God. Even more so, I believe the Christian can reach spiritual completion *as a Christian* with nurturance from the richness of his Jewish roots.

Certainly, there is no more ideal setting for both Jews and Christians to experience this miraculous transformation than in Israel, the Holy Land. For Jews, Israel is the center of the world, their lifeblood as a people. For Christians, Israel is the place where the biblical drama unfolded, where many believe it is yet to be completed, and where their lord and savior walked and carried out his ministry. For both, it is the Promised Land.

Yet, for peace, healing, and reconciliation to come, individuals and nations must embrace dialogue and mutual recognition. And for that to happen, there must be a commitment and sensitivity to looking at each other's ethos and *Weltanschauung* through the other's eyes, and to using the prism the other uses to refract outside reality.

Despite the historical and current tragic record, I believe that religion can be a force for good in the world and that Christians and Jews can work together without compromising their faith. Indeed, in the process of living out our particularistic faith, I believe we can come closer to God.

The Journey Home is my personal testimony. It tells the story of my spiritual journey as a proud Jew and portrays the struggles I encountered along the way. I have written this in the context of a dialogue and emerging friendship with a Christian who was likewise seeking self-actualization and spiritual fulfillment. This is, in almost every respect, a true personal story set against a fictitious backdrop of a walk with Jamie.

My work with the International Fellowship of Christians and Jews, which I founded in 1983 and head, and prior to that with the Anti-Defamation League, is an expression of my profound commitment to the ideal of Christian Jewish fellowship. After twenty-five years in this field, I remain encouraged by the fact that millions of Christians in this country and abroad feel a special kinship with the land and people of Israel and draw great spiritual sustenance and enrichment from them. At the same time, more and more Jews today are altering their historically shaped suspicions and mistrust of Christians, and fostering, in their place, a spirit of cooperation and understanding with them.

I am grateful to those friends, Christians and Jews, who believed in and shared my vision for the Fellowship—some from the very beginning when I launched one of the first ever Evangelical-Jewish conferences in the world, and who continue to this day to stand by my side, often in the face of adversity.

To my IFCJ staff, board of directors, and supporters, and to the many Christian and Jewish "Jamies" I have encountered along my journey, I give thanks from the bottom of my heart. Their friendship, confidence, and trust in me— along with my deep belief that God is somehow guiding my path and calling me to serve him in this, admittedly unorthodox, way—has sustained me at moments of despair and continues to give me the strength to persevere.

To my parents, Simon and Belle, and my family both here in America and in Israel, I owe many things, not least of which is the love they imbued in me for *Eretz Yisrael*, Israel. As the reader will learn from reading this book, it is this love that guides my writing, inspires my heart, and brings pathos, meaning, and sweet fulfillment to my life.

Baruch Hashem, shavti habaita. Thank God, I have returned home.

CHAPTER ONE

THE JOURNEY BEGINS

"Why do they rock back and forth?" Jamie asked, pointing to the Orthodox Jews praying at the Western Wall. The afternoon sun bathed the scene in a warm mellow glow. The praying men seemed in a trance as they rhythmically swayed from side to side.

"That's our way of connecting with God," I responded. "Much like a Buddhist will use a mantra for focus, a Catholic a rosary, and a Moslem beads, we rock back and forth to get into the prayers and find our rhythm with God. There is a biblical reference for this practice: "All my bones shall say, LORD, who is like You?" (Psalm 35:10).

"That's interesting." Jamie frowned. "Jesus did the same thing."

"And what is that?" I asked, my patience with this know-it-all wearing thin.

"Validate ideas with a scriptural reference."

"That was in true Jewish form," I responded like the good guide I was trying to be, surprising him by placing Jesus in a positive Jewish framework. "Orthodox Judaism believes that everything has its source in the Bible—'*Turn it around and inside out and everything is in it,'* says the Talmud. In fact, the mystical strand of Judaism maintains that God created the world *after* creating the *Torah,* which is the primordial blueprint for life. In other words, the world conforms to the *Torah*, not the reverse!"

Jamie was, by now, accustomed to my turning things upside down for him and getting him to see things from a radically different perspective, a Jewish perspective.

יְהֹוָה

Our journey together had begun a few days earlier in New York where Jamie was a journalist for *Currency*, a prestigious financial magazine. He was assigned to write a series of six feature articles on Israeli society as it approached the millennium. His editor, Brent Edwards, told Jamie he was the most capable journalist they had on the foreign beat. Actually, I think he was chosen because he was not Jewish and could ostensibly bring a more objective, dispassionate analysis to the subject. The magazine's editor, who happened to be Jewish, was known in professional circles for maintaining that a Jew could not write objectively about Israel. He would see a Jewish journalist who depicted Israel in a favorable light as lacking in objectivity and unable to overcome his affectionate bias for Israel.

As we embarked on our journey, I wondered whether I could trust Jamie to write fairly and favorably of the land and people I loved so dearly, or would I, by showing him around Israel, perhaps be an unwitting accomplice to his writing a skewed, even harmful, portrayal of her.

Jamie was a seasoned reporter, one of the best in the business. Over the years, he had traveled to some of the most remote countries and the hottest trouble spots in the world. But he had never been to Israel. I had read his column for years and admired his spunk and provocative, no-nonsense writing. So I wondered why he tried so hard to get out of this assignment, especially since he had no family to rush home to, not even a dog. Jamie actually seemed to have an antipathy and distaste for Israel. Something about it made him distinctly uncomfortable.

From the beginning he made it clear to me that he would do his job, gather the facts he needed, pump me for information, and return home. No schmaltz. No pretenses. No politically correct formalities. Definitely no lasting relationships, with me or with the people of Israel who were the focus of his series.

Frankly, I wasn't much happier about being paired up for a week with him. Although we were the same age, forty-eight, we had little else in common to bind us together for nine days. My job was to be his guide, to show him around the country. Israel was, after all, my ancestral homeland, the love of my life. But what, I wondered, would this quasi-cynical, non-Jewish journalist write about her? I had to introduce him to her and protect her at the same time.

The fact was, I owed the editor of his magazine a favor for having given my daughter an internship a few summers earlier. Yes, I did say to him that if there was ever anything I could do to return the favor he shouldn't hesitate to call me. He was now taking me up on my, frankly, less-than-genuine offer.

"Please show Jamie around Israel," Brent asked. "Be his guide, his interpreter. Heck, be his friend."

While I love traveling to Israel and have done so many times, this was the first time I was visiting there with a Christian—a journalist who didn't want to be going in the first place. The only thing we shared was our begrudged obligation to go and our mutual desire to get it over with quickly!

My assignment was to show Jamie the Jewish and Christian sites, to give him a glimpse of the land and to explain its people and history. I was to help him get a feel for the pulse of the nation as it entered the new millennium.

Jamie's job was to write about Israel, not so much about the political situation there, which gets enough coverage in the press every day, but about the pathos of this tiny nation's enigmatic people who, despite their small numbers, capture the imagination and attention of the world scene.

יְהֹוָה

"Tell me about yourself, Jamie," I asked after we got seated comfortably in the plane.

"Not much to tell," he responded curtly, avoiding my eyes and glancing out the window.

It was going be a long, tedious flight and partnership.

"If we're going to be together for a week, I really ought to know something about you."

He turned and looked at me full in the face. "Let's make one thing very clear, Rabbi."

"Please skip the formality and call me Yechiel," I said.

"To tell you the truth, *Rabbi* is a lot easier to pronounce than *Yech-, ch-, ch-, Yekiel*."

"Jesus, your lord, would have had no trouble pronouncing my name. He was a Jew, you know." I hoped I didn't sound patronizing, but he really did need a tutor.

"Yes, I know. But that doesn't faze me much," he said dismissively.

"What do you mean by that?"

"I'm not really big into my Christianity anymore. I grew up Baptist, but—"

"Then you're a Baptist," I interjected brightly, glad to have that one clue to his background.

"You could say that. But, frankly, I'm not sure I'm a Christian."

"What do you mean you're not sure you're a Christian? You just said you were brought up a Baptist. Doesn't that mean you are a Christian?" He was splitting hairs and equivocating at the same time.

Jamie shifted in his seat and drummed his fingers on the armrest.

"I was born a Jew," I continued, warming to the professorial role and not giving him a chance to respond, "so I'm a Jew. I can be more or less observant. I can be Orthodox or Reform or nothing at all. But I always remain a Jew. Is that not true for Christians?"

"Christianity isn't something we're born into like you Jews are born into Judaism." He sighed. "It's something we *accept*. And I never really accepted Jesus as my personal Lord and Savior."

"I don't understand," I said.

"You see, being Christian is different from being Jewish," Jamie said, rolling his eyes and dripping with noblesse oblige. "I'll bet you think Hitler was a Christian, right?"

"Well, yes. He was a Catholic who was never excommunicated from the Church despite his horrific deeds. So I guess he was a Christian, a bad one to be sure, but a Christian nonetheless. Unlike Martin Luther, I might point out, who was, in fact, excommunicated by the Church, not for murdering people as Hitler did, but for espousing unacceptable theological views. Don't you find that bizarre, to say the least?"

"That's another matter," Jamie answered. "My point is that all the Jews I know—and working in New York I know quite a few—believe that if you're not a Jew and are not a

Buddhist or a Muslim, you are a Christian. Almost by process of elimination. That's why you Jews have such a persecution complex. You assume that everyone who hates you is a bona fide Christian.

Jamie was treading on dangerous ground.

He continued in a rising voice, "You Jews think that everyone in America, except for Jews and Muslims, is Christian. In fact, you identify Christians today with those who persecuted you throughout history. Tell me I'm wrong," he declared.

Before I could respond, he continued his tirade.

"But those weren't *real* Christians," he belted out so loudly the flight attendant came over to ask if everything was all right.

"What do you mean those weren't Christians?" I asked, incredulous.

"Those were Catholics," he said with an exasperated shrug.

"Aren't Catholics Christians?" I asked in utter astonishment.

"Not exactly. Certainly some of them are. But the fact that members of the Catholic Church did what they did to Jews over the centuries proves that they were never really Christians in the first place." He looked at me as if I might be too dense to grasp this complex concept.

"I don't understand," I said softly, attempting to calm him down. People were beginning to stare at us. "If a Jew sins, he's still a Jew, albeit a sinful one. If the Church acted wrongfully in the name of Jesus—and it certainly did—I can perhaps understand your defending it by claiming its actions did not represent what Jesus would have advocated. But does it follow that those people who persecuted Jews were not Christians? They worshiped Jesus, obeyed his word as written in the New Testament, and even slaughtered Jews in his name and for his sake. You may want to whitewash the evil they did by saying they were misguided and sinful. But how can you, in effect, grant them and their Christian faith absolution by saying that they were not Christians in the first place?"

It was pure sophistry on his part of the most offensive kind.

"Most evangelicals," he continued, "would certainly insist that's the case. They would tell you that throughout the past two thousand years, at least until Martin Luther came on the scene and the Reformation got underway, there was always a secret underground church that constituted the true Church of Jesus Christ. The Catholic Church that we know, whose attitude toward Jews was so despicable in the past, reflects neither the true Church, authentic Christianity, the views of genuine Christians, nor the real Jesus Christ."

He folded his arms and gazed at me confidently as if this settled the matter.

"I must admit, I am totally confused," I said indignantly and somewhat shaken. "In one fell swoop you absolve the Church of centuries of anti-Semitism by saying that those who killed, tortured, and expelled Jews were never *really* Christians in the first place. You are essentially suggesting that Christians are not responsible for their evil actions because by doing them they prove they aren't really Christians! That's a cop-out."

I wasn't going to let him off the hook just to preserve the peace. This was just the kind of casuistry that lay beneath so much Jewish-Christian animosity.

"Aren't Christians and the Christian faith, as interpreted and practiced by its adherents, responsible for the evils of the Crusades? Inquisitions? Expulsions? Pogroms? Can we speak of the integrity of a true Christian witness in some noetic, abstract realm when, over the centuries, the practitioners of that faith consistently carried out evil in its name? And is the evil performed by Christ's followers simply a misinterpretation of true Christianity and the fault of its human practitioners, or, when repeated for centuries, does it not reflect negatively on the very essence of the faith itself? Isn't a faith that lends itself to such evil intrinsically flawed?"

Jamie stared out the window as if he weren't listening. The flight attendants were wheeling the beverage cart down the aisle. I wasn't about to be distracted, though, from making my point.

For the first time in my life I was able to imagine what it must have been like in the Middle Ages when Jews were forced, on pain of death, to engage in no-win disputations with Christian authorities. It didn't matter what the Jews said. There was no way to penetrate the Christian conviction that they were ipso facto in the right and Jews were just plain wrong.

"I'm not saying I agree with this evangelical stuff," Jamie said defensively. "But I do know that while Hitler, to you, is a bad Christian, to me and to Evangelical Christians, he was not a Christian at all. That's not a cop-out. That's just the way it is."

"You mean, that's the way you believe it is," I said. Could he really be this obtuse?

Ignoring me, he continued. "You Jews transpose your own categories onto us when, actually, we have a different set of self-definitions. You assume that just because you are born Jewish, we are born Christian. But that's just not the case."

"Are you telling me that Jews don't even know what makes Christians Christian?" I replied in total exasperation.

"That's right," he said. "You know how *you* define us, but not how we define ourselves."

"So tell me, bottom line. Are you a Christian or aren't you?" I really needed to know where he stood, what value system undergirded his living in the world.

He squirmed in his seat as if struggling for the right words. "Kind of."

"What does that mean?"

"I told you. I grew up Baptist, but I'm not sure what I am now. I'm like your three-day-a-year Jew who goes to synagogue only on the High Holy Days. I don't go to church all year long—maybe on Christmas and Easter. I guess you could say I'm a two-day-a-year Christian."

"Are you a fundamentalist?" At least if he believed in the inerrancy of the Bible we'd have something in common.

"No."

"Evangelical?"

"No."

"Are you born again?"

"I told you," he said with exaggerated patience that was beginning to get on my nerves. "I'm not even sure I'm a Christian. Besides, do you even know the differences among those groups? Most Jews I know lump them all together and see them negatively as 'the Christian Right.'"

I had to agree.

"That's a fair accusation. Why don't you explain the basics of all those terms to me."

"It's a long story, but," he said, taking a deep breath, "we're stuck here together on the plane for the next several hours, so here goes.

"To begin with, evangelicals have three main distinguishing theological characteristics. First, they believe in the centrality and inerrancy of the Scriptures, usually as interpreted literally. Everything you need to know is in the Bible. Second, they believe in the born-again experience. And third, they regard it as their duty, or great commission, to share this good news with the world."

"I've read a lot about this born-again phenomenon," I said. "Exactly what does that mean?" I was getting a bit of an idea of how opaque, if not incomprehensible, Jews and Christians could be to each other.

Jamie seemed preoccupied, but answered after a pause. "It means that at a certain point in your life you accept Jesus Christ as your personal Lord and Savior."

Thinking maybe that acceptance might be like a revelation or epiphany, I said, "You mean on a certain day and time?"

"Yes, though I never had that all-defining, life-changing experience, at least not that I can remember. I admit I wish God would reveal Himself powerfully to me. That would certainly clear things up for me." He smiled wryly. "Were that to happen, I would feel no choice but to believe in Him. Unfortunately, that hasn't happened and I doubt it will. I am too rational for all that stuff. So I am your average, culturally Christian pagan," he said with a grin.

"Then," he continued, "there are the charismatics and Pentecostals, premillennialists and postmillenialists, pre-tribulationists and posttribulationists, and—"

"Hold it. You lost me," I said, stopping him. "This is getting too heavy for me." I suddenly felt very tired. "I need to get some sleep."

I turned away, still wondering whether this journalist I'd just met, and would be spending the next week and a half with, was a Christian or not. I was still confused about who is, and who is not, a Christian.

Had I been totally misguided all these years by my pre-conceived notions based simply on conventional wisdom? Could I, in fact, be ignorantly lumping together all Christians and seeing them as contemporary links on the chain of an ancient Christian tradition whose anti-Semitic adherents murdered my ancestors? That would make me a Jewish mirror image of the Bible-thumping, thick-skulled Christian stereotype that much of the media caricaturize.

I was confused and worn out. One thing was certain—it was going to be a long few days.

יְהוָֹה

Our Lufthansa plane stopped in Frankfurt, where we had a few hours to kill. We deplaned to stretch our legs and get a change of scenery. I also had my morning prayer obligations to fulfill. "What are you doing?" asked my surprised travel companion as I draped myself in my *tallith* and put on my *tefillin*.

"I'm praying," I said. "The sun has risen and I must say my morning prayers. I've never missed a day since my bar mitzvah. I'm not about to now."

"But why are you putting those straps with boxes on your arm and head? Why the shawl? Do you have to do it right here in the transit lounge in front of all these people? Everyone is staring at you like you're from another planet. Seems like that's something you should do in private."

"I put on my tefillin—the little boxes—because that is what the *Torah* teaches us to do. It says, 'Bind them as a sign on your hand and let them serve as a symbol on your forehead.' As for the *tallith* or prayer shawl, the *Torah* says, 'Attach a cord [tassel, or *tzizit*] of blue to the fringe at each corner. . . . look at it and recall all the commandments of the LORD and observe them.'"

"But must you put that on right here in public?" Jamie was clearly embarrassed.

"I have no choice," I said with seeming equanimity. "There's no place private for me to go."

The truth is, I *do* feel awkward calling attention to myself like that in public. But what made me feel even more uncomfortable was the fact that I was praying in Frankfurt, Germany. I had never before set foot in Germany. I was haunted by memories of the Holocaust that happened right there, in that place, just a few decades ago. It all seemed so incongruous. And surreal. Could those people have done those horrible things right there? I simply could not grasp the reality of what had happened sixty years ago.

As I *davened shacharis*—prayed my morning prayers—the image of a group of Nazis taunting a rabbi praying with his prayer shawl and phylacteries came to mind and tormented my spirit.

But Hitler did not win! In spite of all of the atrocities, he did not succeed in obliterating the Jews or in eliminating Judaism. The Jewish people and their witness continue to live, even in the Lufthansa transit lounge. I was in Germany, alive, praying the very same prayers, wearing the same ritual objects, and facing the same direction, east, toward Israel as did the murdered rabbi some sixty years ago.

CHAPTER TWO

OUR FLIGHT

I finished my prayers, and Jamie at last recovered from his embarrassment. We boarded the plane and left Germany behind, along with my memories of the cataclysmic Jewish past for which it was the staging ground. We were on our way to Israel, the land God promised Abraham four thousand years ago, the inheritance of the Jewish people, our future destiny. We were traveling back to the future.

Breakfast was served when we hit cruising altitude. Both of us were starved.

"Why are you getting different food from me?" Jamie asked, sounding a little annoyed.

"Because I keep kosher," I said, opening my napkin.

"So then is my meal impure?" he asked with a note of sarcasm.

"Not exactly," I said patiently, not wanting him to launch into one of his speeches just now. "But as an observant Jew, I try to fulfill the biblical teachings of what I may and may not eat."

"But this is Lufthansa, not El Al," he insisted.

"Yes, that's true. But people can order special meals on most airlines, such as fish, fruit, vegetarian, or salt-free. I order kosher. The flight attendants are even trained not to open the sealed food tray until I give them the okay to do so. That way I can be assured it was not tampered with."

An impish look came over his face. "I can't wait to get to Israel and eat a big juicy ham sandwich," he said, trying to provoke me. Or tempt me, I'm not sure which.

"You'll have a tough time doing that," I answered, completely unruffled. "There are only a handful of places in all of Israel where you can buy ham."

There is no significant demand for ham among Israeli consumers. As secular as many Israelis are, even most of those who don't keep kosher the way Orthodox Jews do will not eat ham, bacon, or shellfish. These remain repugnant, if not to their theology, to their basic Jewish sensibilities.

"In fact," I challenged him, "you'll have a tough time finding a restaurant that will serve you a glass of milk or butter with your dinner since we are prohibited from mixing milk with meat."

"Hold it!" said Jamie, "you can't pull that one on me. I've read the Bible too. You're always citing it as a source for your laws. Where does it say anything about not drinking milk with meat?"

"You're right," I admitted. "Over the centuries, the biblical prohibition of 'You shall not boil a kid in its mother's milk' was extended by the rabbis to include mixing meat—and even chicken is included in this category of meat—with milk products. They also went so far as to prohibit eating them at the same time and even using the same dishes and utensils."

"I guess that's why many Jews have separate dishes for meat and dairy, right?" said Jamie. "I once ate over at an Orthodox Jew's home, and he made a point of telling me that."

"That's also why observant Jews wait a few hours after eating meat before having dairy products," I added. "Most Israeli hotels, which are under rabbinic supervision, observe these kosher rules."

"Incidentally," I continued, "that's also why from Friday evening to Saturday night on *Shabbat,* which is Hebrew for *Sabbath*, the cooks, switchboard operators, and all the rest of the hotel staff are non-Jews, most often Arabs or foreign workers. Jews are prohibited from working on *Shabbat,* and hotels would lose their kosher certification if they violated these rules.

"The power of the Orthodox rabbinic authorities, who have complete control and jurisdiction over such ritual matters, is so great that they threaten to revoke the kosher certification of hotels that are, in fact, strictly kosher, but which host things like Christmas parties or New Year's Eve dances. This is seen as smacking of Christian influence and, as such, a violation of the biblical injunction, 'You shall not copy the practices'—in other words, the ways of the goyim or gentiles."

"But Israel's not a theocracy," Jamie said with a note of irritated defiance. Stabbing the air with his fork, he asked, "Why do the rabbis have so much clout?"

"Religion is at the very core of the nation's ethos. Moreover, the question of what is Judaism's rightful place in society is a central one, much like the situation with Christianity today in the United States. But unlike America, which was not established as a Christian nation per se and which has a history of separation between church and state that is codified in law, Israel's situation is more complex. For while Israel is a democratic Western nation, it is also a Jewish one, embodying the vision, struggles and age-old dreams of a particular faith community, the Jews.

"The late Yitzhak Rabin, during his first tenure as prime minister, was actually removed from office because of, what would certainly seem to us to be, a trivial incident that arose from this question."

"What happened?" Jamie asked between bites of his omelette.

"A squadron of F-14 fighter planes that had been purchased from the U.S. arrived in Israel on a Friday afternoon, a few hours later than expected. Before parking them in their hangar, the Israeli pilots demonstrated a series of air maneuvers for fifteen minutes, by which time it was sundown, the Sabbath. The air force had publicly violated the Sabbath in a situation that did not involve a life-and-death threat, when all the Sabbath laws are suspended. Because they did so in the presence of the prime minister himself, which gave these actions the tacit endorsement of the government, the religious parties bolted from the coalition and the government fell."

"That's incredible. The whole government fell because of that?" Jamie wore an expression as if I were describing life on Mars.

"Yep. Incidentally, that's also why Israeli officials who may be unobservant in their personal lives do not violate laws such as the Sabbath and kosher when acting in their public and official capacities.

"Israel, in short, is struggling with its soul—how to be both a democratic *and* a Jewish state. There are those who stress the former and others the latter. There are those who believe Israel is a state *for* Jews, especially those seeking refuge from anti-Semitism, and ought to be secular in nature and religiously neutral. And there are others who insist that the Jewish state ought to reflect and be guided by the religious laws or *halakhah* of the Jewish people. It is a real dilemma tearing the nation apart, even more divisive than the critical question of how Israel should make peace with her Arab neighbors."

"But most Israelis seem to be quite irreligious," said Jamie. "It doesn't seem fair that their lives should be controlled by the Orthodox minority."

"Israel's political system lends itself to such a situation," I had to admit. "The Orthodox parties, which have been part of every government since Israel's founding in 1948, exert tremendous pressure on the issues of primary concern to them. And since the coalitions in power have tended to govern with a slim margin, parties will threaten to leave the government if their demands are not met. They have incredible leverage.

"But you should also be aware that there are gradations of Orthodoxy on the religious spectrum, with some being more fundamentalist or *Haredi* than others. Most Israelis, Jamie, can best be described as traditional, observing rituals like kosher and the Sabbath, but not with the same degree of strictness and meticulousness as the Orthodox. They may not attend synagogue regularly or keep kosher laws strictly, but they study Jewish history and archeology, and daily affirm their Jewish identity in their routine lives. Unlike nonidentifying American Jews, who are often indistinguishable from the rest of the populace, Israelis celebrate the Sabbath and the various other holy days, perhaps not in the same way Orthodox Jews do, but in some meaningful manner nonetheless."

"I'll never figure you Jews out," Jamie said. Rather condescendingly, I thought.

"You'll get the hang of it soon enough," I said, more out of politeness than honesty. The flight attendant had taken away our trays and was now offering us hot towels.

"What about Conservative and Reform Jews? Don't they exist in Israel?" Jamie asked, rubbing a towel through his hands.

"Not in a big way. They are really American movements, although they are making inroads here. But it's hard to import nonindigenous groups and ideologies into Israel, especially since they're seen by the Orthodox, and even by most secular Israelis, as inauthentic and advocating a watered-down form of Judaism. The joke here is that the synagogue that secular Israelis do not attend has got to be Orthodox.

"That is why in Israel there is no religious middle ground as there is in America. One is either Orthodox or secular, to varying degrees. It's a polarized and dangerous situation, a powder keg ready to explode."

"Who controls civil matters relating to personal status such as birth, marriage, divorce, and death?"

"All those areas are regulated by the rabbis," I said.

"I presume you mean Orthodox rabbis," Jamie said, leaning forward in his seat and trying to follow me closely.

"That's correct. Here, the Orthodox rabbinate has exclusive control over religious matters. That's why, for example, a non-Jew seeking to marry a Jew in Israel can only do so if he or she is first converted by an Orthodox rabbi. By contrast, in America a Conservative or Reform rabbi could marry the couple, even if a non-Orthodox rabbi had converted them. So, too, a man who is a *Kohen*, meaning he is from the priestly tribe, who wants to marry a divorcée, cannot do so in Israel since the *Torah* expressly prohibits such marriages. The couple must travel out of the country, usually to Turkey or Cyprus, and get married there since Orthodox rabbis will not perform such marriage ceremonies, and they are the only ones authorized to register Jewish marriages in Israel."

"How about a homosexual marriage?" he asked, trying to find some inconsistencies or injustices inherent in rabbinic authority.

Before I could even respond, he bleated out, mimicking me, "I know. That's the paradox of a democratic Jewish state, the struggle for the Jewish soul."

"You see, Jamie," I answered with an ironic smile, "I told you you'd get the hang of it. Actually, in many respects a Christian pastor in Israel has greater religious freedom and authority than Conservative and Reform rabbis. On the other hand, a few months ago, three Messianic Jewish families—that's Jews who believe in Jesus—"

"Yeah, yeah, I know," Jamie said wearily, interrupting me.

"Anyhow," I continued, "they were almost forced to leave Israel even though they had lived there for many years on temporary visas. One of them, I understand, even had a son who had served in the Israeli army."

Jamie looked honestly baffled. "Why would Israel want to kick those people out? After all, they're Jews. And isn't the *raison d'être* of Zionism that all Jews are allowed to live there?"

"Not exactly. Meyer Lansky, the Jewish mobster, was not granted citizenship, not that I agree with that decision nor that I think his situation is analogous to that of Messianic Jews. But the point is, there *are* limitations on the right of Jews and non-Jews to live here, though far fewer than those in the American immigration and naturalization process where criminal elements and even people with AIDS are not allowed to enter, let alone take up citizenship.

"But you are correct," I pushed forward with my explanation, "about Zionism promising every Jew a haven in Israel. In fact, the first act of the Israeli Knesset when Israel was established in 1948 was to annul the notorious British White Paper that barred Jews from entering what was then Palestine. The Knesset supplanted it in 1950 with the 'law of return,' entitling Jews to automatic citizenship immediately upon their arrival."

"I knew that," Jamie said somewhat arrogantly. "I majored in poli sci in college and focused on twentieth-century British foreign policy. I also know that England controlled Palestine before 1948, and even about the Balfour Declaration of 1917 that was the first document legitimizing the idea of a Jewish state."

"Wow. I'm impressed." I could be excused if I answered his sarcasm with my own, I thought, under the circumstances.

"I even know about the Peel Commission—"

I stopped him mid sentence and said, "That's enough for now, let's eat supper."

"Okay, pass the ham and cheese," Jamie said, teasing me again.

Over dinner, I explained to Jamie the basics involved in one of the most difficult and volatile issues facing Israel.

"At the crux of Israel's religious-secular divide," I explained, "are the negative perceptions the two groups have of each other. Secular Jews see religious Jews as trying to impose their restrictive values on the rest of society by fiat and legislation, while religious Jews see their secular counterparts as trying to erode, and even eradicate, the uniquely Jewish character of the nation.

"Every few years, Jamie, an issue erupts that brings the two forces at loggerheads. In Israel, the ideological and religious forces are organized into political parties. The battle inevitably enters the political arena and, at times, spills over into the streets, creating those clashes we see occasionally on the evening news between secular and Orthodox Israelis.

"Intra-religious disputes can be fought over the seemingly most trivial and minute of issues, like whether or not a movie theater, drugstore, or public transportation would operate on *Shabbat*, and even whether private cars may travel through religious neighborhoods on holy days. A few years ago, a prestigious dance group, which was to perform in skimpy costumes at Israel's fiftieth-anniversary program, was barred from appearing on stage because of pressure from the religious parties."

Jamie looked dumbfounded. "Do you mean to tell me there is no public transportation on Saturday in Israel?"

"Not exactly, Jamie. First, you have to remember that for Jews, the Sabbath is not only on Saturday. It begins an hour before sundown on Friday afternoon and ends an hour after sundown on Saturday. This is derived—"

He put up his hand to cut me off. "Let me guess, from the Bible," he said dryly.

"That's right. The *Torah* states that, after each day of creation, 'there was evening and there was morning.' Since every word of the Bible is believed to be divine, the order is deliberate, indicating that the day begins and ends at sundown, not at midnight as we know it."

"But why the extra hour before and after the Sabbath?" he asked.

"Good question. We extend the Sabbath at both ends to show our love for it, eagerly welcoming it earlier and sadly prolonging its departure. Much like a bride and groom who long to see each other and spend as much time together as possible, so is the Jewish people's love affair with *Shabbat*.

"The truth is," I admitted, "the issue of buses operating on *Shabbat* is far more complicated than I am describing. Back in 1948, David Ben-Gurion, the prime minister of the new nation, tried to stop both the religious and the secular sides from imposing their will on the other by establishing a policy referred to as 'the status quo.' He froze the religious situation as it was then, and prohibited any changes from being made as to how religion would be observed by the state. And since buses did not run on the Sabbath in Jerusalem in 1948, though they did operate in other cities like Haifa, that became the law of the land, even to this day."

"Because that's the way it was in 1948," said Jamie, shaking his head in dismay.

"That's right. Preserving the fragile, delicate balance between the religious and secular elements of Israeli society forestalled the eruption of a feud that could have led and, God forbid, could still lead, to a fratricidal battle. Incidentally, for the same reason, all religious girls, as well as those religious boys who study in a *yeshiva* or seminary, are exempt from serving in the Israeli army, though the issue keeps coming up in the Knesset and before Israel's Supreme Court."

"All because that's how it was in 1948?" Jamie said in disbelief.

"Correct. Of course back in 1948, Jamie, there were just two or three thousand men exempt for religious reasons. Today, there are some thirty thousand claiming a religious deferment and not serving in the army. That is a huge number for such a small state.

"It's not hard to understand why this issue is a major source of tension between the religious and secular factions. The former see such exemptions as necessary to ensure the continued Jewish character of the nation; the latter view the exemptions as a means to effectively dodge civic responsibilities yet still benefit from the life-and-death sacrifices of others."

"Sounds to me like Khomeini would have felt comfortable there," Jamie said chuckling. "Israel may not be a theocracy in name, but it sure appears to be one in practice."

"That's the struggle Israel faces," I said, ignoring his, facetious, I hoped, comment, "of being both a Jewish *and* a democratic state. It is a paradox that Rabbi Meir Kahana, the assassinated founder of the Jewish Defense League and Kach Israeli political movement, said was actually a contradiction and an impossibility to reconcile.

"The truth is," I went on, "this question of the rightful role of Judaism in society is the ultimate challenge facing the people of Israel today. How it is handled will determine the fate of the nation. Jews are an ancient yet modern people, exiled from their land for two thousand years, who miraculously returned to reclaim that land, restore their language, rebuild their cities, recover their dignity, and inspire a worldwide peoplehood.

"It is the historic opportunity and responsibility of the nation of Israel to be in dialectical tension, holding on to both poles—the old and the new, the distinctively Jewish and free democratic—without abandoning either."

"And trying, at the same time, to be a normal people," Jamie interjected, his chin on his hand.

"That's right. But what is *normal*? Herzl, the founder of modern Zionism, envisioned a normal Jewish state as one in which the police, the firemen, and even the prostitutes would be Jews. But that kind of normalcy was achieved decades ago and has today been found wanting in the sense that it is not sufficient to keep both factions away from each other's throats.

"Yet while Israel desperately wants to be normal like other countries, she still carries with her the prophetic dream and biblical calling to be a 'light unto the nations,' a witness of God's love to the world, the standard-bearer of justice and compassion. Israel strives to build a society transcending normalcy, to shine in a unique way—in medicine, science, technology, ethics, and the like—despite her having had to live her short life in a bad neighborhood where, to stay alive, she had to exert raw power.

"And while she seeks acceptance among the family of nations," I continued, "it is not at the expense of her demise. 'Better to be alive and unpopular,' Golda Meir used to say, 'than dead and pitied.' Better to accept the biblical curse invoked by Balaam, 'They are a people that dwelleth alone and not thought of by the gentiles,' than to seek approval from the nations of the world and pay the price of national annihilation.

"Even the educational system in Israel reflects this struggle for the nation's soul, this dialectical tension inherent in a modern, Jewish, democratic state. Here, even the secular public schools teach the Bible, not as the word of God, of course, but as the historical record of the Jewish people."

"Wait a minute. I don't understand something," challenged Jamie. "Why is it that in America, Jews are among the most ardent, vociferous opponents of such things as teaching the Bible, praying in public schools, and even posting the Ten Commandments in schools, courtrooms, and other public places? Why aren't American Jews more sensitive to the struggle for the *American* soul that is fighting the same battle between secular and religious values? Seems like there's a disconnect here. I mean, what's good for the goose should be good for the gander."

"Well," I responded patiently, for at least he seemed interested in understanding, not just setting me up for criticism, "the American Jewish community is, by and large, liberal and mostly secular, and the organizations that represent them are proudly such. Most are deeply committed to an absolutist interpretation of the First Amendment and principle of the separation of church and state. In their view, America was never founded as a Christian nation the way Israel was established as a Jewish state. Rather, the founding fathers intended to create an American society that is neutral with regard to religion and is devoid of religious practices and symbols in the public square.

"And there's another reason why Jews in America have such strong views on this matter," I continued. "They are mindful of their history of persecution under theocratic governments that sought to impose Christianity on them, and are fearful they could suffer the same fate in America were religion, namely Christianity, permitted to be established in the public arena.

"People like Pat Robertson and Jerry Falwell and groups like the Christian Coalition frighten Jews. They believe that were the Christian Right to gain power in America, they would reverse the civil liberties Jews and other religious minorities now enjoy, and would attempt to impose Christianity on society. Jews, unfortunately, also tend not to distinguish between the religious right and the political right."

Jamie looked me right in the eye, gauging, I guessed, the degree of my sincerity. "I notice you speak of these matters in the third person. Do you not share that perspective?"

"To be completely candid, Jamie, I don't. I certainly do not advocate the imposition of Christianity or even generic religion on anyone. Yet I believe that the obsessive Jewish paranoia with the Christian Right—and the overzealous American Jewish commitment to expunging all semblance of our Judeo-Christian values from society—often masks a more deep-seated fear of religion per se than hostility toward Christianity. Many of those staunchly opposing a greater role for religion in the public square simply do not wish to have their agnostic or atheist views—which also need to be protected—become something other than the established norm. So they camouflage their concerns in lofty constitutional garb.

"I myself don't believe that a naked public square, in which all vestiges of religion are removed from public life, reflects a neutral posture toward cultural values. Secularism is a concrete value in itself, much like religion is in the opposite way.

Moreover, I am convinced that our founding fathers and constitutional framers never intended for religion to be totally absent from public life but rather that it not be imposed on nonbelievers."

"I guess you could say that most Jews don't see eye to eye with Pat Robertson, Ralph Reed, and Jerry Falwell on this matter," Jamie joked. "You, of course, being a notable exception."

"That's an understatement. But while I disagree with them on many things, I think all Americans owe them a tremendous debt of gratitude. They boldly and courageously remind us that our nation has strayed from the lofty values on which it was founded and which have guided it over the past two centuries. They are correct, in my view, in maintaining that the wall of separation between church and state that the courts have, in recent years, built up, is too high. The pendulum is definitely in need of a corrective swing to the center.

"The truth is," I said, "I'm grateful to Christians like Pat, Ralph, and Jerry for reminding us of our seminal biblical, Judeo-Christian heritage, albeit often in ways that make us cringe. They challenge us to confront the kind of society we have become, and I applaud them. I don't believe that placing the Ten Commandments in our schools or having a moment of silence in classrooms will eliminate the scourge of violence, drugs, teenage pregnancy, and immoral behavior that engulfs us. But I do believe that such actions are a start toward creating an environment conducive to more responsible, moral behavior."

"And how do you see the situation in Israel?" asked Jamie.

"Well," I answered, "liberal American values are certainly widespread in Israel today—for good and for bad. But so far, the country has been largely spared the moral relativism and cultural equivalence so pervasive in America today. Israelis remain passionately judgmental and opinionated about their values, rarely adopting the attitude so common in the U.S. that whatever one does is okay as long as it doesn't hurt anyone."

"I would imagine," Jamie interjected, "that these Israeli attitudes can have a harmful side effect of creating an environment of intolerance between the religious and secular."

"You're absolutely right," I responded. "And it's painful to see. I imagine it's just a matter of time before the moral ambivalence so evident in America will reach Israel's shores and chip away at the moral fabric still tenuously in place. But meanwhile, they have just the opposite problem, dealing as they must with a society constricted by narrowness and intolerance."

After blurting out these remarks in the heat of the moment, I hoped I had not maligned my people or given Jamie a distorted picture of the religious beliefs and values of the Israeli nation. It was important that I explain.

"I believe deeply that by living in the Jewish state and risking their lives to defend it, even these secular Israeli Jews are casting their destiny with the Jewish people and demonstrating through their deeds that they are, in fact, *religious*, though not necessarily *observant*. Indeed, no matter how many times an Israeli soldier might say, "I don't believe in God, I don't believe in God," his actions speak louder than his words. By serving in the Israeli army, he proclaims himself a Jewish believer who cares for his people and lives his life in sacred partnership with the God whose existence he may be so quick to deny.

"This is one of the most profound mysteries and instructive lessons associated with the birth and continued existence of the State of Israel, Jamie: God was able to use *all* sorts of people—religious, antireligious, communists and socialists, agnostics and atheists—to bring about this miracle. Indeed, religious Jews were a minority among the founders of the nation. Yet God was able to use all his children as instruments of his power in the unfolding of his divine plan. Even if they don't recognize it or want to believe it."

"I doubt this conciliatory view is very popular among the Orthodox there." Jamie remarked.

"Unfortunately, you're right. But there have always been some rabbis throughout the generations whose love for Israel—the land and the people—and belief in God's love for his children serves as a paradigm for such beliefs."

At this point we were both exhausted by the trip and arcane theological conversation and took out our sleeping pills to settle down for a nap. There would be plenty of time for us to get more acquainted.

CHAPTER THREE

WELCOME TO ISRAEL

As we stepped onto the warm, sun-drenched tarmac of Tel Aviv's Ben Gurion International Airport, Jamie turned to me and said, "Am I supposed to bend down and kiss the ground? It's cement!"

"Some people do," I said. "When this is the moment they fulfill their lifelong dream." I felt a profound change the second I arrived in this sacred land. There was something empirically different and palpably holy about this place. The air seemed fresher, purer, replete with history, and pregnant with meaning.

I looked around at the other passengers disembarking from the plane. They were young and old, bearded Orthodox rabbis along with Christian pilgrims, people speaking all sorts of languages—English, French, Hebrew, German, Russian, and Danish. We were all, in our own way, returning home, even though most of the passengers had, in all likelihood, never set foot on this ground before. The anticipation and excitement we all felt was obvious in spite of our long, tiring journey.

We had arrived in Israel, the world's greatest melting pot, where people from all over come to fulfill their special vision and mission in life. They come, not so much to relax, but to get a glimpse of the old, be emboldened by the present, and feel the sacred touch of God's presence in the holy stones on which we walked.

יְהֹוָה

The presence of undercover security agents all around us was evident, paradoxically making us feel tense yet secure at the same time.

"You'll soon see them as a natural part of the Israeli landscape," I said to Jamie.

We stepped onto the bus that would take us to the main terminal, the sound of raucous music blasting in our ears.

"Ha," laughed Jamie. We both recognized the loud sassy voice of Tina Turner. "The sounds of the Holy Land! So this is Israel. This is what Jews have been dreaming of for centuries...the land of American rock-and-roll. I thought all I'd hear was 'Hava Nagilah.'" Jamie was excited and interested in everything around him.

We arrived at the terminal where a big sign greeted us: WELCOME TO ISRAEL. We passed through the jostle and hubbub of customs and immigration, and looked for our luggage. I noticed on the board a list of flights arriving at roughly the same time, from Istanbul, Moscow, Paris, Miami, Kiev, and Zurich. I was reminded of the prophecy that one day "all the nations shall stream to Israel." Despite all the security concerns, tourists continued to flock to Israel—not as many as when there will be peace, but more than ever before. The tourism industry was alive and well.

Jews are proud that the El Al pilots are Jewish and that the young, attractive, immigration officials in army uniform, waiting to stamp our passports, are also Jewish. Nice Jewish girls with guns and boys who fly planes. It seems incongruous. Perhaps that is why it is such a great source of Jewish pride. Even the porters, mainly new immigrants from the former Soviet Union, are Jewish. Being a porter is not a traditional Jewish profession. But then Jews are not accustomed to running their own country, at least not for the past two thousand years. For this Jewish nation to function, its citizens recognize they must do all sorts of jobs, not just assume traditional Jewish professions by becoming doctors and lawyers, professors and businessmen, but also farmers and policemen, maids and porters.

"Ah yes, the Zionist dream fulfilled, to become a nation like all others," Jamie said, not without a note of sarcasm in his voice.

"The problem today," I explained, "is that we Jews often refuse such work, seeing it as beneath our dignity."

"That's why such jobs are taken by Arabs, right?" asked Jamie, waving to a tall burly porter across the room to come over and help us with our bags.

"Correct. But when the intifada erupted in the late 1980s and terrorism escalated in the early 1990s, Jews were reluctant to hire non-Israeli Arab laborers, despite dependence on them. This became even more compelling with the outbreak of the 2000 El Aksa intifada. Even trustworthy Arabs who had worked for Jews for years were barred from getting to their jobs in Jewish areas by Israeli army road blockades. As a result, produce rotted on the vines, cows went unmilked, fruit was unharvested, and housing construction came to a virtual standstill. Newly arrived Soviet Jews filled some of these jobs, but most others remained empty. There was a critical need to replace the cheap labor force that Arabs from Gaza and the West Bank had provided since 1967.

"It was then that a decision of historic proportions was made—to import workers from foreign countries like Thailand and Romania to replace the cheap indigenous Arab laborers. These people, you see, were highly motivated by a desperate need for work, and did not constitute a security risk."

"I'm familiar with that process," Jamie said, alluding to his vast experience as a journalist in foreign nations. "Many other countries in the Middle East do the same, including Saudi Arabia, which imports so many foreign workers, especially Palestinians, that they sometimes constitute the majority of the country's population."

"Gee," I said. "I didn't know that."

"Goes to show you, Rabbi, there's always something you can learn from this goyish guy you're with," he said with a smirk.

"Where did you pick that word up?"

"You mean *goyish*? Oh, around. I know that some Jews use it derogatorily, but I assume you're a bit more enlightened."

"I hope so," I responded. "Anyhow, while the problem of cheap labor may have been solved, it created an entirely different set of problems for Israel—a restive Arab population that is heavily unemployed and filled with despair."

"It's that kind of atmosphere that prompts young Arabs to join terrorist groups," noted Jamie. "They're angry, impoverished, and can see no way out of their situation."

"That plus the financial assistance that radical nations like Iran provided them and the spiritual redemption that their religious leaders promised them.

"In any event," I continued, "it has created an Israeli dependence on foreign laborers who came as temporary visitors but now number well over a hundred thousand souls. Moreover, this 'temporary foreign labor pool,' as the government calls it, is settling down and having families. Now they're asking for schools for their children, social services for their needy, better apartments to live in, and so on."

"Sounds like those temporary workers are here to stay," Jamie remarked.

"Certainly does," I said. "But even more disturbing, is Israel's abandonment of one of its central ideological tenets, *torat haavoda*—a play on words, literally meaning 'the Bible of work,' referring to the Jewish work ethic that elevates labor to biblical significance."

"You see what I mean," said Jamie. "You need to learn about the Protestant work ethic from us Christians."

"You're probably right. It's not that Israelis lack a sound work ethic. It's just that today it finds expression in areas like technology, computers, and scientific research. But who will pave the roads? Irrigate the fields? Build the houses? Pick the crops? Milk the cows?"

"And clean up the dung?" added Jamie.

"Even new Jewish immigrants are rarely inclined to engage in such 'demeaning' work. And so Israel finds herself in a predicament of her own making. She is dependent on temporary foreign workers who are increasingly feeling more permanent and at home here, who are demanding to be treated with greater dignity, and who could significantly affect the social fabric and ideological work ethic of the nation."

"Quite a problem," reflected Jamie. "But I'm sure you Jews are smart enough to come up with a solution, and, I hope, a humane one."

I wondered for a moment if Jamie was poking fun at the stereotype of Jews as being more devious and cunning than smart, or whether he believed the canard himself. I decided to ignore his remark.

"A half-century after the founding of Israel," I continued, "there is another ideological premise of early Zionism that has been shattered—the belief that the advent of a Jewish state would lead to "normalization" for the Jewish people and the elimination of anti-Semitism from the world. Israel has achieved many things in her short lifetime. She can be relied upon to come to the aid of imperiled Jews anywhere, be they blacks in Ethiopia or hostages in Entebbe. But her existence has not brought about the sought-after normalization that would eliminate the scourge of anti-Semitism from the world."

"Actually," said Jamie, "I think it's the opposite. I have found that the very existence of Israel has provided bigots with a more convenient way to express their hatred of Jews under the guise of the newfangled form of anti-Zionism. It's not *de rigueur* to express anti-Semitic sentiment in the West today. But it remains acceptable to camouflage such views in the form of anti-Zionist diatribes."

"Very astute," I pointed out, surprised at the degree of his insight. "In fact, even the horrors of the Holocaust, which Jews felt would certainly jar the world into a new sobriety and make anti-Semitism an obsolete relic of humanity's dark past, have faded and lost much of their sting. The generation of Holocaust survivors is dying out, leaving us bereft of witnesses to preserve the authenticity and memory of that cataclysmic event.

With all the museums, books, educational programs, and blockbuster movies on the subject, a shocking number of young Americans remain ignorant of those events and dangerously susceptible to the influences of anti-Semitic revisionists who deny its ever having happened."

"It seems pretty clear," said my non-Jewish companion, "that the birth of Israel has not eradicated anti-Semitism from the world stage."

"Nor has the Jewish people's normalization been fully achieved," I added. "Indeed, little about Israel's history can be described as *normal*. But neither can its destiny."

"What exactly is Zionism?" Jamie asked.

"We could talk about that for weeks, Jamie. Essentially, Zionism is the political movement giving expression to the age-old Jewish dream of returning to *eretz yisrael*, the land of Israel. Rooted in late twentieth-century political nationalist thought, it calls for a return of the Jewish people to the ancient biblical homeland of Zion, what we today call Israel.

"The classical Zionist position, especially as articulated by Israel's founders like David Ben-Gurion, is that Israel ought to replace the diaspora as the home for the Jewish people. Of course, most diaspora Jews disagree, and see a legitimate place for them outside Israel."

"How do you feel about this matter?" asked Jamie, looking me straight in the eye.

"Let's see if you will be able to tell me where I stand on this by the time we go home," I said, knowing my feelings would be no secret by then.

"What is the difference between *exile* and *diaspora*? asked Jamie.

"*Exile*," I explained, "reflects the Jew's inability to return to his homeland; *diaspora* is when the Jew chooses to live away from his homeland."

"So today Jews live in the *diaspora*, not exile, since if they wanted to, they could simply hop on a plane and move to Israel. Right?"

"Correct." He was an apt pupil when he wasn't baiting me. I continued my exposition on basic Zionism. "Tension has long existed between two points of view. The first point of view insists that, to be a true Zionist, a Jew must physically live in Israel. The second point of view says that a Jew can live outside Israel so long as he expresses his Zionist fervor by supporting Israel financially, politically, and in other such ways."

"You mean, vicarious Zionism?" Jamie asked.

"Kind of. Jews were divided on this issue already back in 586 B.C.E. after the Babylonian Jewish exile. While some Jews returned to Israel fifty years later when Cyrus of Persia conquered Palestine from the Babylonians and invited the Jews to return, many chose to remain in the diaspora."

"I notice you keep saying 'B.C.E.' after certain dates," Jamie observed. "Don't you mean B.C.?"

"No, Jamie. We Jews are reluctant to use terms like B.C. and A.D. that define time in terms of Jesus' birth and death. Instead, we say B.C.E., an initialism for Before the Common Era, and C.E., for the Common Era."

"Interesting," said Jamie. "I never heard that before. Anyhow, where do most Jews come down on the issue of what constitutes true Zionism?"

"Most reject the Ben-Gurion paradigm and view Jewish life in America as legitimate. They believe they can be full-fledged Zionists living in the U.S. Most Israelis, of course, disagree. In their view, the establishment of the Jewish state brought the exile to a close and delegitimized Jews living outside Israel. For them, there is no excuse for Jews not to move to Israel today. That's why, if we get the chance to visit the Diaspora Museum in Tel Aviv, you'll notice how the exhibits end abruptly with the establishment of the State of Israel in 1948."

"How do you feel about that?" persisted Jamie. He seemed determined to sound me out on my own attitude toward Zionism.

I shrugged. "You tell me next week before we leave."

יהוה

Although I am a proud American, I agreed with the Israeli point of view on this matter, though I wasn't about to trust

Jamie with that information yet. To be complete and ful-filled as Jews, I believe we must live in Israel or, at least, dream and plan for the day we move there. It is wrong, in my view, to accept diaspora living, either in its *de facto* or certainly in its *de jure* form.

Rarely does a day go by when I do not feel tension, dis-comfort, and even guilt for not living in Israel. It is terribly difficult to pray every day for God's return to Zion and not do so myself. It is extremely painful to read in the prophets of God's promise for a Jewish return to Israel and not seize the historic opportunity before me to do so myself.

To be sure, God is present in America, and most Americans who emigrate to Israel maintain dual citizen-ship. But the Bible teaches clearly that Israel is *sui generis;* that is, Israel is qualitatively different from all other places in the world. Here God manifests His special divine provi-dence all the time. His presence, in the words of the *Torah*, can be felt over this land "from the beginning of the year until the end of the year."

This tension among Jews on how to understand the true meaning of Zionism has bedeviled diaspora-Israel relations for decades. Quarrels have erupted over the years when, for example, American Jewish leaders, feeling secure and some-times smug in their Zionist credentials, publicly criticize particular Israeli policies, and Israelis tell them to butt out since they do not live in Israel and would not suffer the consequences of their policy recommendations. Again, I agree with the Israelis. In my opinion, diaspora Jews forfeit their right to criticize Israeli policies, especially publicly, no matter how much money they donate to Israel.

The tension between diaspora and Israeli Jews is not a new one. It existed, for example, between Babylonian and Palestinian Jewry both before and after the destruction of the second temple in 70 C.E. The struggle has centered on the question of whose religious and political authority should prevail. Put differently, in the absence of a papal-type hierarchy, who speaks for the world Jewish community? Until recently, the diaspora Jewish community was actually stronger, more organized, and more Jewishly learned than their Israeli counterparts. But while this balance of power may have been true for the first five decades of Israel's existence, today there has been a marked shift favoring the Israeli side.

יהוה

My welcome to Israel—one of my suitcases was lost.

"Don't worry," a blasé clerk said to me, "It will show up... eventually."

I stood impatiently in a long line—not my first encounter with Israeli bureaucracy—and joined in playing the country's favorite game: hurry up and wait.

A lone man stood behind the counter, slowly servicing at least a dozen exhausted travelers, all waiting quietly, almost reverently, in line to retrieve their lost luggage. After a few minutes, I lost my patience and decided to leave.

"Let the concierge from our hotel deal with it," I said to Jamie, my prickly new acquaintance.

As we passed customs and walked into the big welcome hall, hundreds of people bearing flowers, hugs, and smiles were waiting to greet their relatives. It's inspiring and heartwarming to see the ingathering of Israel in practice, and not simply to read about it as a prophecy in my Bible.

Chapter Four
The Taxi Ride

As Jamie and I left the airport in a cab, the warm rays of the sun and a magnificent view of the mountains greeted us. The sun and the mountains are two similarities between Israel and California—a fact not lost on countless Israelis who move to America and settle in Los Angeles.

But a plaque outside the main terminal building quickly reminded of where we were. The plaque memorializes the Kozo Okamata massacre. Japanese terrorists murdered twenty-six people—ten Israelis and sixteen Puerto Rican pilgrims—in the airport on May 30, 1972. Security at the airport has been beefed up ever since, and there has been no additional terrorist attack. Thank God...and the IDF, the Israeli Defense Forces.

Seeing the memorial plaque was a rude awakening for Jamie and me. Frustrations like the bad food on the plane, the poor in-flight service, my lost luggage, and the question of when I would have fresh clothes took on a new perspective. I pointed out to Jamie that virtually everywhere we traveled we would see monuments to those killed in that place. Monuments commemorating tragedies from the past threatened to overspread this land of milk and honey, I explained. They are stark reminders of how every inch of Israel is *terra sancta*, to be tread upon consciously, conscientiously, and appreciatively. Yet while the earth bears witness to the agonies of generations, I assured Jamie that it also bears fertile promise for the children of the future.

"From afar, Israel probably seems like a perilous, even frightening place to live," I said. "Actually, it is safer walking around the streets of Jerusalem and Tel Aviv than in the downtown area of most major cities in the U.S.

"A few years ago, when I was in Chicago, I remember hearing on the radio of a terrorist attack in Jerusalem, and calling a friend who lived there to see if he was okay. Coincidentally, he was just about to call me out of concern for *my* safety after reading a report in the Israeli papers of a shooting in a Chicago suburb that left five people dead. I guess it's human nature to adjust to the reality we know, and feel anxiety over the situation we can only imagine."

On the highway, we passed a convoy of flatbed trucks carrying tanks covered by camouflage netting. We saw a group of young men and women, rifles slung over their shoulders, standing on the side of the road.

"Soldiers on leave, hitching a ride home," I explained to Jamie, preempting his question. "People here stop for soldiers since most everyone was, at some time or another, a soldier himself or herself, and probably has a family member or friend in the army now. The country is so small, the driver is even likely to know the hitchhikers or, at least, share a common friend."

In the distance on the right, we saw mountains and rolling hills lush with green fields. On the left, the terrain was brown, dusty, and barren. The contrast was striking. Our driver explained that the road we were driving on cut through the *territories*, the Israeli term for land conquered in 1967 and often referred to as the West Bank, though most Israelis refer to it by the biblical names of Judea and Samaria. Noting the obvious difference between the cultivated and the barren fields, the taxi driver continued, "Of course, we're not yet finished developing this area but, in time, we will be."

Jamie turned to me and asked forthrightly, "Aren't you scared a terrorist might come out from the fields and attack us on the highway?"

"Highly unlikely, Jamie," I said with Israeli bravado. "Besides, after a while, you don't even think about that. People here conduct their lives with as much normalcy as possible. You can't live with constant fear of terrorism on your mind."

יהוה

Visiting Israel is quite different from taking a relaxing vacation in the Bahamas. It's more like an intensive study mission. Everywhere one treads, especially in Jerusalem, one walks on history. Literally. One of the greatest problems Jerusalem's planners face is that almost every time they begin paving a road or digging a hole, they uncover antiquities that, according to Israeli law, must be preserved.

"A few months ago a riot erupted near the hotel where we'll be staying," I explained to Jamie, "when construction workers building a highway found bones there. A group of *haredim*—the ultra Orthodox Jews—tried to prevent the bulldozers from moving in since the bones may have come from an ancient Jewish cemetery, in which case, according to Jewish law, they cannot be disturbed.

"You see that mound over there?" I continued, pointing out the window to what I knew was actually a garbage dump. "It could very well be a *tel*."

"What's a *tel?*" Jamie asked with utmost seriousness. I was starting to feel guilty for leading him on, but, heck, I decided to have a little fun with him.

"I'll explain. Since land in Jerusalem is scarce and has been viewed as sacred for millennia, each civilization utilized the limited space by building on top of the remains of prior generations. In the words of Jeremiah, "The city shall be rebuilt on its mound.""

"There you go again," Jamie said.

"What?" I asked.

"Speaking like Jesus by citing a biblical source every time you open your mouth."

"Okay, I'll accept that. Anyhow, if you dug down into that mound over there"—I was starting to feel really guilty for leading him on, but it was so much fun—"you could very well uncover the ruins of five, ten, even twenty different civilizations going back thousands of years. I hope we'll visit Megiddo, which Christians refer to as Armageddon, where this phenomenon is especially evident. There's also a wonderful museum with a replica model of the Megiddo tel that demonstrates this clearly. But you really should understand a basic fact about archeology here in Israel: Each civilization is built upon the prior destroyed one. The deeper one digs, the further back in history one is actually going."

"Thank you ever so much, my excellent guide," he said sarcastically, probably in response to the pedantic tone of my remarks. "But let me teach you something, Rabbi. That 'tel' over there you pointed to? It's actually a garbage dump."

Just as I realized Jamie was only playing along with *me* all this time, my thoughts were suddenly interrupted abruptly and my heart skipped a beat, actually a few beats. The car on our left swerved into our lane, barely a yard in front of us, to avoid an oncoming car. Our driver took it with aplomb and continued driving as if nothing happened.

The pace of living in Israel is fast, as is the aggressiveness, and even macho recklessness, encountered here, especially on the roads.

"People here think they're in their army tanks, driving with almost total abandon and lack of consideration for others," Jamie blurted out in alarm.

"Indeed," I said, "Add to that the frustrations and anxieties of daily life, ninety-degree or higher heat most of the year, many cars without air conditioning, and old, unsafe roads, and you have a formula for disaster. Did you know that far more people die and are injured in car accidents in Israel each year than in terrorist attacks? While new attention has been given to public safety—more speed traps, better roads, more driver education, and so on—and the situation is certainly better today than it was just a few years ago, the problem remains vexing."

We could see out our window more young boys and girls, most looking barely eighteen years old, going about their business routinely, carrying Uzi submachine guns and M-16 rifles. Already the sight was less jarring to Jamie, particularly since he had traveled to many countries with a similar situation.

"I hope I never stop noticing those young kids with guns and that I never become inured to it," I said.

"Nice thought, Rabbi," said Jamie. "But for the foreseeable future, that's an unrealistic pipe dream. But, then again, where would we be without dreamers reminding us of what's possible? You're right. It is disturbing to see young kids with M-16 rifles, and I, too, hope I never lose sight of that."

יְהוָֹה

We passed the Valley of Ayalon where, according to the Bible, Joshua halted the sun from setting so that he could continue winning the battle. Suddenly, I heard Jamie ask, "What's that over there?" Shaped onto the field, by harvesting only portions of the wheat, were the Hebrew words *lo zazim min hagolan.*

"It says, Jamie, 'we will not be moved from the Golan.' You see, here in Israel, politics is even etched into the flora; its influence impacts everything.

"And take a look over there," I said. "That's an old Benedictine monastery. Incidentally, they make great liqueur. And over there are remnants of the Israeli border-police station that played such a critical role in the battle for Jerusalem during the 1948 war. And take a look at the rocky, mountainous terrain all around us, Jamie. Can't you just imagine young King David prancing around these hills with his sheep, writing the beautiful Psalms, and hiding from Saul, maybe in one of those very caves over there?"

Jamie stared at the scenery around him and didn't respond. He was just starting to take it all in. After all, this was pretty heavy stuff. But under his breath I could hear him mutter something like, "Yeah, but did young David prance around with an M-16?"

יְהוָה

No matter how many times I visit Israel and drive up and down her hills, I immediately feel linked with my people and bonded with my ancient past. Jamie brought an end to my pleasant musings with a vengeance.

"Listen, Rabbi, I am here to do a story on the Israeli people and their values, to feel the pulse of this nation, not to tour the sites and hear lectures on every rock's history. Anyway, I'll probably forget ninety percent of everything you're telling me by tomorrow."

"Hey, Jamie," I said soothingly, trying to calm him down. "If I'm going too fast and the experiences are too compelling, I'm sorry. But to understand the Jewish people you cannot sever their nexus to the history of this country. This land has molded the Jews into the people they are."

Jamie looked at me silently and then turned to the window and gazed outside. He was beginning to take in the land and its painful history.

We passed Herzlia, Israel's Silicon Valley and home to some of the top Israeli computer firms. Once known for her Jaffa oranges, Israel today is at the cutting edge of technological innovation, scientific research, and medical advances.

But Israelis are also known for falling well behind Western standards in service and marketing. For years El Al Airlines was the paradigm for this—and brunt of many a joke—because of its poor service and the I-don't-give-a-damn attitude of its personnel. The concept accepted as gospel in America—that the customer is always right—was a difficult principle for proud and independent Israelis to accept. To their credit, this attitude has changed dramatically for the better in recent years.

We passed Bab el Wad, a dry *wadi,* canal, where many Jews died defending Jerusalem in 1948, and began our trek in third gear up to the Holy City.

"Now you'll see why the Hebrew word for 'moving to Israel' is *aliya,* meaning 'going up,'" I said. "As you can see, the road to Jerusalem is literally *up*lifting, physically and spiritually. Many Jews died on this road trying to break through the Arab siege of Jerusalem in the 1948 War of Independence. Israeli convoys carrying food, water, and medicine tried to reach the besieged defenders of the city, which was surrounded by enemies perched on the heights above. To this day, I can remember exactly where I was and how deeply the book affected me when I read *O Jerusalem*, which described that 1948 battle."

"Yes," said Jamie proudly. "The power of the journalist."

I decided to let the distinction between journalist and author pass, and allow Jamie to bask in his moment of pride. "I also still recall traveling this road on my first trip to Israel when I was thirteen. The trip was my bar mitzvah present from my parents. Of course, then it was a very narrow, treacherous two-lane road, nothing like the wide, paved six-lane highway it is today."

On the sides of the highway, left as a memorial to those who died in the Battle for Jerusalem, are the actual burned-out convoy trucks that were destroyed in the war. But as we approached a curve, I noticed something I had not seen before, a large steel-girded fence at the edge of a cliff, with rocks piled up on top of one another.

"Why the fence and rocks?" I asked our driver.

"They were put there as a memorial a couple of years ago, after the terrorist attack that forced a bus off the road at this spot," he said.

I remembered the incident well. Quite a few passengers were killed in the attack. Despite my being a regular visitor here, I was reminded anew of how everything in this land bears witness to ongoing struggle and sacrifice; even mundane items like fences, stones, and roads are imbued with blood and a sense of ultimacy.

יְהֹוָה

Jamie and I had barely slept for almost two days. But weary as we were, we were too excited to fall asleep in the taxi. We made another turn up the mountain and there, in the distance, we saw lights.

"Is that Jerusalem?" Jamie asked excitedly, straining to see around the driver up the road.

"What you see," I said hesitatingly, "is one of the new suburbs created after the 1967 war in an area that used to belong to Jordan. The entire area, which, incidentally, was totally barren beforehand, is what the American and European press often refer to as 'settlements in the occupied territories.'"

I was relieved Jamie didn't start engaging me in a political discussion on the issue. I was much too tired for that. Besides, I had a feeling we'd have an argument about it, and our relationship was still too tender for that.

Three minutes later, as we turned another bend, we could see an area with even more lights in front of us.

"What's that?" Jamie asked.

"That's downtown Jerusalem," I replied.

"Do you mean to tell me that before 1967, Jordan was so close to Jerusalem? It looks like no more than ten minutes by car from there to downtown Jerusalem."

"I can tell you exactly," said our driver, a former tank commander with the Israeli army. "That suburb is eight minutes by tank and about ten seconds by plane from the heart of Jerusalem."

I shuddered at the reminder of how vulnerable Israel was before the city was reunited in 1967.

"There's no way Israel should give up that land to the Arabs," Jamie declared. "I don't care if U.S. policy calls it occupied Arab territory. It would be suicidal for Israel to jeopardize her security by giving it up. A totally irresponsible act."

I sat in silence without responding. What was happening to this new acquaintance of mine? Were those overtones of compassion and sympathy I detected in his voice?

The view around us was breathtaking. We had arrived in *Yerushalayim,* the "city of peace," the city that has rarely seen peace. I had returned home.

I recited the traditional prayer of *shehechiyanu*, thanking God for keeping us alive, sustaining us, and enabling us to reach this glorious day. For centuries, Jews died hoping to reach this place, dreaming of a moment like this when they could see Jerusalem. They prayed, as Jews throughout the world and I still do, *leshana habaah biyerushalayim*, "next year in Jerusalem." But for me that day, the dream was a reality. There I was, as the Bible describes it, with my legs firmly planted at the gates of Jerusalem. I wondered why my generation was the one privileged to see this two-thousand-year-old dream fulfilled. Certainly, we were the least deserving.

"Let me tell you something about myself, Jamie," I said as we approached the city. "My father and grandparents were born here in Jerusalem. They emigrated to the United States in 1929 at the height of the Arab riots. I come from a line of many generations, and I am the first to be born outside Israel. When my grandparents died in New York, we followed the Jewish custom of burying them here in Jerusalem."

"That way, when the messiah comes and the resurrection of the dead takes place, they will be among the first to be resurrected, right?" interjected Jamie.

"How did you know that?" I asked, surprised.

"I must have read it somewhere," he said dryly.

The traffic slowed to a standstill.

"What's up ahead? An accident?" Jamie asked.

"No, a security check," I answered.

Because of the continuing threat of terrorist attacks in Jerusalem, cars are routinely stopped and checked before entering the city. We were finally waved through the checkpoint by the guards. We rounded one last curve and found ourselves right smack at the central bus station.

The roads in Jerusalem are too narrow to accommodate the new reality of city traffic. That explains the countless fender-benders and traffic jams. There's no way the city planners could ever have imagined sixty or seventy years ago that Jerusalem would become the bustling city it has.

Most first-time visitors, influenced by Bible stories they learned as children, envision Jerusalem as filled with camels and buggies, not cars, trucks, and motorcycles.

יְהֹוָה

Dazed by the crowded streets and endless streams of cars, Jamie asked, "How do Israelis afford cars on their meager salaries?"

"That is the best-kept Zionist secret no one can figure out," I said, "particularly since the government adds a twenty- or thirty-thousand-dollar import tax to the cost of a car.

"People here live their entire lives in debt, Jamie," I continued. "Even if they spend twenty years pulling themselves out of debt, as soon as their children get married, the custom here is to provide them with an apartment and go back into debt, or overdraft as they call it. Actually, I'm very proud of this, even though it probably doesn't make good economic sense. It reflects one of the most cherished Jewish values guiding Israeli society today and is captured best by the beautiful adage *hakol bishvil hayeladim,* everything for the children.

"Including living one's entire life in debt?" challenged Jamie. From the look on his face I could tell he thought this was a sacrifice that didn't make sense.

"Yes," I said, emphatically. "Here the people live for today, if only because inflation, which at one point reached almost two hundred percent, takes such a big bite out of people's incomes. Paying a bill two weeks late can actually save people an enormous amount of money."

"I once wrote a column," Jamie said, "on the psychological effects runaway inflation has on people. Obviously, it leads them to spend the little money they have rather than to save it, since they know it will be worth less tomorrow."

I chuckled. "This mentality is so ingrained in Israel that people used to joke that it was cheaper for them to take a cab than a bus because with cabs you pay at the end of the ride."

"Why are all the buildings made from the same stone?" Jamie asked, looking around.

"That is the law," I explained. "A decision was made by the British mandate authorities in 1918 to preserve the beauty of the city and to ensure a uniform skyline by insisting that all buildings made from then on be from Jerusalem stone."

"You'd think the homogeneity would be boring and dull," said Jamie. "But I can see how it enhances the beauty of the city, especially at this time of day, as the rays of the setting sun ricochet off the stones of the buildings."

יהוה

Beep. Beep. Beep. The radio blasted from the front of the cab: *This is Kol Yisrael from Jerusalem. The time is eight P.M., and here is the news.*

Israelis are obsessed with the news. Even in public buses, the hourly news is turned up so everyone can listen. The words everyone dreads hearing came across the speakers: *Today two soldiers were killed in an ambush in southern Lebanon, and three others were wounded.* An eerie quiet gripped the passengers, a solemnity that took Jamie by surprise.

Jamie stared silently into the distance.

"Welcome to a typical day in Israel," I said.

CHAPTER FIVE

ARRIVAL AT HOTEL

We reached the King David, our beautiful five-star hotel, and checked in. The luxurious and cosmopolitan atmosphere impressed Jamie. I walked up to the desk and told the concierge about my missing luggage.

"You shouldn't have left the airport without it!" she chastised me. "But don't worry, we'll look into it. I'm sure you'll have it back in a few days."

"A few days!" I exclaimed in exasperation. That was completely unacceptable. "Please see what you can do to get it here quicker," I pleaded. "This is a tremendous inconvenience for me!"

As soon as we finished checking in, Jamie turned to me and said, "Let's find a good bar and have a drink. I'm buying!"

"Good luck," I said. "Here in Israel there really isn't a bar scene like we have in America. They're much more sophisticated and European. Here the jet set—and jet set wannabes like you and me—sit around at outdoor cafés, eating and drinking espresso."

"Sounds like Saudi Arabia to me." A spark of recognition came to Jamie's eye. "I spent two months there and wasn't allowed to drink a bit of alcohol. Of course, *somehow* I managed," he said with a wink, confirming my suspicion that alcohol could be obtained illicitly even there.

"Not at all," I countered. "You can buy alcohol here, even at the cafés. You just don't have the same kind of culture of people going to bars to drown their sorrows over a drink, or even coming together socially to have a martini with friends. Israelis are much more inclined to sit around over coffee and cake, or to go out for an ice cream than they are to go to a bar for a drink."

"That explains it," said Jamie with a little smile.

"Explains what?" I asked.

"That explains why so many of us gentiles have this stereotype of Jews as being—and please don't be offended by this, but it's a common perception—that Jews are short and fat."

"Really?" I was shocked. "I didn't know that's what they say about us. Well, we Jews have our stereotypes of you gentiles too. In fact, for centuries, Eastern European Jews poked fun at their gentile persecutors by invoking the pithy Yiddish maxim, *Shikur iz der goy.* Non-Jews are drunks."

Jamie whistled softly. "Gee, that's very tolerant and enlightened."

"I didn't say it was. And I am not defending it by any means. But, for whatever reason, Jews didn't have the problem of alcoholism that the Irish, for example, had. Whether it was because they lacked the genetic predisposition to it or because wine was used for Sabbath rituals and not seen as taboo. Whatever the case, such taunts toward *goyim*—a term that literally means nations and refers to non-Jews but that, as you pointed out earlier, can also be invoked pejoratively—were in vogue for a long time."

"And still are among some of you Jews," interjected Jamie, shaking his head.

"True," I answered. "But by way of explanation, such derogatory comments were usually the only available weapons Jews had to fight against the anti-Semites around them. Jackie Mason has a funny routine highlighting this difference between Jews and gentiles. He says in his own inimitable way that the first thing a gentile says when he attends a wedding or bar mitzvah party is, 'Where's the bar? I need a drink.' Jews, on the other hand, ask, 'When is dessert being served?' In fact, and I'm hanging out our dirty laundry with you now, it used to be that when Jews planned a reception and were figuring out how much liquor to serve, the caterer would ask how many gentiles were attending."

I could tell Jamie was beginning to get annoyed. He was staring rigidly ahead, avoiding eye contact with me.

"Today, of course, the situation is quite different. Jews in America are virtually indistinguishable from non-Jews on this matter of drinking."

"Yeah," said Jamie calmly, "we're all equally a bunch of lushes!"

We were both too hyper from the long flight and our new surroundings to sleep, which would have been the sensible thing to do, so we decided to go for a walk to relax. As we reached the corner, we saw two young male soldiers, one with his arm draped over the other's shoulder affectionately.

"Love is in the air," Jamie began to sing. "I see you allow gay soldiers in the Israeli army. Do they have an ask-but-don't-tell policy here too?"

"They're not necessarily gay, Jamie," I replied. "Nonsexual physical contact among people of the same sex is quite common here in Israel, perhaps because of the Middle East cultural influence. It may also be because these boys and girls enter the army and live in close quarters together for a few years. They are likely just close friends who put their lives on the line for each other every day and express that camaraderie physically as well as emotionally."

"Ah, the quintessence of Epicureanism!" Jamie exclaimed grandly with a flourish of his arms. "Live life to the fullest in the here and now, for tomorrow we may die."

"I imagine there's some truth to what you say, Jamie, though I'm not quite as cynical about it as you are. In Israel one can't count on tomorrow the same way one can in the States. Life is far more tenuous. Maybe that's also why there is pathos and *joie de vivre* here that one doesn't often see back home. These people feel the need to live for today, not in an Epicurean sense, but more in the Buddhist ethos of being fully conscious of life, living in the moment, and not taking tomorrow for granted."

Strolling around the city, we were struck by the abundance of parks and the fact that the parks were filled with people, even at this late hour of the night. I remembered how shocked an Israeli friend of mine visiting New York was to learn that most parks there closed at sundown.

"Can I drink the water here?" Jamie asked, as we passed a public water fountain.

"Sure," I replied. "It may take you a few days to adjust to it, but it's okay. Water is a serious matter here in Israel, as you know, Jamie. In fact, experts believe that future wars in the Middle East will erupt over who controls the sources of water and main aquifers."

"And it is certainly a key issue in the peace negotiations with Syria," added Jamie.

We returned to our hotel and settled into our comfortable, attractive suite. I beat Jamie to the shower.

"Hey," Jamie called from the bedroom, "the TV has only three stations. Well, at least one of them is CNN. You know you're not too far from civilization when you can turn on the TV and see CNN news."

"The heck with TV," I chided. "Where else in the world can you take a shower and see right outside your window the Temple Mount and place where Abraham, David, Solomon, and Jesus walked?"

I watched the birds resting on the ledge outside my window and wondered if they realized how privileged they were to be in the Holy Land. What? There I was ascribing such thoughts to birds!? Was I going totally insane? No, I assured myself. It is just a bout of Jerusalem syndrome, an actually diagnosed psychological malady affecting tourists and citizens alike, especially in this millennial period.

What is it about this exotic land that can lead a rational person to feel overpowered by God's presence... and become a lunatic mystic overnight? Otherwise normal people can go off the deep end and believe they are the heavenly incarnation of ancient prophets. Could this be the same affliction that gripped Yigal Amir before he so casually, cruelly, and almost hypnotically murdered Prime Minister Rabin?

Walking had given us an appetite, so Jamie and I went downstairs to the hotel restaurant, which even at that late hour was filled with tourists. As we waited to be seated, we overheard a Jewish couple from Argentina speaking Spanish. Another family was speaking English with a British accent (or maybe it was South African—I can never tell the difference), and a young man was speaking French.

The waiter came over and asked if we'd like to order a drink. "I'll have a Pepsi," said Jamie, careful not to order a hard drink after my earlier chiding.

"And I'll have a double scotch," I say. "Nothing wrong with drinking in moderation."

"Sorry, no Pepsi," said the waiter to Jamie with an air of indignation. "We only serve Coke here."

"Many places in Israel don't serve Pepsi," I explained to Jamie as the waiter walked haughtily away. "Israelis are still angry at Pepsi for cooperating with the Arab boycott for so many years and for refusing to sell their product in Israel. Now that Pepsi wants to sell here, many stubbornly refuse to buy.

"Pepsi also had a major public relations fiasco a few years ago," I continued, "when they tried to crack the Israeli consumer market. It launched what it thought was a brilliant billboard campaign throughout the country.

"In a series of different frames, the advertisement showed an ape evolving through various stages until finally becoming a blond surfer boy holding a can of Pepsi. The soft-drink company's marketers were attempting to show the evolution of consumers' good taste. They assumed that what's cute in America would also go over big in Israel. They were wrong. In Israel, the campaign was a disaster.

"Secular Jews saw it as a devious attempt to capture the Israeli market now that the Arabs had revoked their boycott. The religious community saw it as a promotion of the doctrine of evolution against creationism.

"The marketing mavens should have known better in dealing with the ethnically diverse and religiously hypersensitive Israeli public. In another incident a few years earlier, dozens of bus shelters in Jerusalem were destroyed or defaced by ultra Orthodox Jews who were offended by a series of ads posted on their walls showing women in skimpy bathing suits."

"Zealots from the middle ages," cracked Jamie.

"Perhaps they're people like you and me seeking to protect their children from being exposed to such influences. For this reason, many Orthodox Jews don't have a television set in their homes. These people have a system of values they don't want compromised or corrupted, and certainly not against their will in public places where they don't have a choice."

"I am sympathetic to their desire to preserve their sacred values," said Jamie. "But I doubt they'll have any greater success than other groups have had. That includes fundamentalist Moslems in Iran and Afghanistan who also want to protect their society from being corrupted by Western influences like television, film, and the Internet, which they believe contributed heavily to the moral decay in America. And the fact is, Rabbi, that even insofar as the Christian Right's influence in America is concerned, I don't believe they or any other group can totally separate itself as an island from modernity and not be exposed and ultimately swayed to these values, for good or bad. They will either have to reject them, embrace them, or adapt them to their own *Weltanschauung* or world-view."

יהוה

The number of Christian pilgrims visiting Israel always amazes me. One sees them everywhere. Statistics reveal that over fifty percent of the tourists to Israel are Christian. They come for all sorts of reasons—the sun, to visit the holy sites and bond with the land, to watch the Bible come alive before their eyes, and to walk where Jesus walked. The experience they have in Israel is almost always an extraordinarily gripping one they remember all their lives.

Most Christians tour Israel with their church and pastor, in contrast with Jews, who travel with their family or in a tour group rather than with their synagogue and rabbi. This is because Christians, who define themselves by their faith, are linked to Israel, first and foremost, by that faith. It is their belief in Jesus and the Bible that prompts them to visit the Holy Land and thereby reclaim their biblical spiritual roots. While Jews, too, are bound to Israel by their faith, they are tied to it, perhaps even more, by their history and culture, which are indelibly linked to that land, and by their profound attachment to Jewish peoplehood, which reminds them of their collective destiny here.

The incongruity of the two groups' purposes (and itineraries) in touring Israel is striking. Christians, seeking to retrace the footsteps of Jesus, visit Christian sites like Capernaum, the Stations of the Cross, ancient churches, and Gethsemane. Jews, seeking to link up with their people and history, go to the Western Wall, Yad Vashem, Masada, ancient synagogue excavations, and so on.

At times their paths cross, which is not surprising since they share so much in common, including the sacredness with which they regard the city of Jerusalem, the Hebrew Bible, and our history from Abraham to Jesus.

But while they are brothers and sisters in this land, they remain distant from one another, going separate ways, visiting the sites holy to their own particular faith community, and only rarely getting a glimpse of how those from other groups experience the land. There is a vast gulf between them in the way they view and experience this land, despite the fact that for both communities it is holy ground. We may pass one another in the hotel, wait in line together for the same restaurants, and walk the same promenades, but rarely do we acknowledge the other's presence, let alone interact.

Most Jews are shocked to learn that the majority of tourists to Israel are Christian. And they are incredulous that so many millions of those Christians see Israel as *their* homeland. They just do not grasp that millions of Christians feel they are returning home to *their* Jewish roots and to *their* spiritual center.

This is true not only of those Pentecostal Christian Zionists who believe that the biblical promise of the ingathering of the Jewish people to Israel is a sign of the end times, but for Christians of all kinds.

Christians feel at home in Israel.

יְהֹוָה

In the middle of our dinner, across the room in the restaurant, a Christian tour group from Mexico sang songs about Jerusalem in Spanish.

After dinner, we visited the shops in the lobby. Jamie bought a T-shirt with a picture of an Israeli boy waving an American flag and these words: DON'T WORRY AMERICA, ISRAEL IS BEHIND YOU.

"I still find it hard to adjust my expectations," said Jamie. "I really thought Israel would be more like the Jewish version of Afghanistan than the modern, sophisticated, industrial society it is. I know it's unreasonable, but a part of me expected to see biblical figures walking around wearing sandals and robes, with camels and donkeys in the streets. I just can't get the Sunday-school images of Israel out of my mind."

"Don't worry, Jamie," I reassured him. "I think we all feel a little let down by the reality here, especially the fact that not everyone is a saint or prophet. That's why it's so important that when you write your series on this nation and its people you have a realistic view of them. See them for who they are, the remnants of Israel who have risen like a phoenix from the smoldering ashes of Europe to begin life anew in their ancient homeland. Understand them for the community they have become, a people who have made a collective vow not to grant a posthumous victory to Hitler, who sought to destroy Jewish life. Before you set pen to paper, know that, ultimately, all these people want from life is to live in peace."

I was embarrassed by my homiletic tone, but reassured by Jamie's warm smile that he understood my concern for what he would write. His warm smile reassured me that he would not let me down.

יהוה

The King David Hotel is where diplomats and dignitaries often stay. It is famous not only for its luxurious rooms and elegant service but for what happened there in 1948. The Israeli underground bombed the hotel, which then served as headquarters for the British archives and top brass. Ninety-two British officers and soldiers were killed. To this day, the saboteurs, headed by Menachem Begin who later became Israel's prime minister, insist they made a telephone call warning of the impending bombing but that it was arrogantly dismissed by the skeptical British, who were certain their headquarters was impenetrable.

The hotel became a national landmark and symbol to the world, first and foremost, of the national Jewish resolve for freedom and independence, and later, of the elegant accommodations Israel could provide visitors.

יהוה

"What's with all those couples drinking Coke in the lobby?" asked Jamie. "They all look alike—the guys with their black suits and black hats, the girls with their long skirts and long sleeves."

"Those are *shidduchs*," I responded. "You'll see them in lots of Jerusalem hotels."

"What's a *shidduch*?" Jamie asked.

"Well," I said, "it's essentially a matchmaking date for young Orthodox men and women, who generally seek to get married by their late teens or early twenties and who do not believe in dating. They're also forbidden by their rabbis to go to parties or dances, so someone sets them up."

Jamie's eyebrows went up. "You mean like the matchmaker in *Fiddler on the Roof?*" he asked.

"Essentially. They'll meet in a public place like a hotel lobby and spend a few hours talking. If they like each other and believe the *shidduch* has potential, they'll go out a few more times and talk some more. If there's still interest, they'll meet each other's parents who, by that time, have thoroughly checked them and their family out. If the parents give their approval, the couple will get engaged and married a few months later. Having *yichus*—meaning they come from a long line of important family members, especially rabbis—helps, though today, it plays far less a role than in the past. And if the father of the bride is wealthy enough to buy the young couple an apartment and support them while the groom continues his *Torah* studies, that is usually a deal clincher."

"Is that how you met your wife?" asked Jamie earnestly.

"Not exactly," I said. "I met her at the pool right back here in 1973."

"How romantic," Jamie said. "Hey, the night is still young. Let's go someplace, why don't we?"

"Okay," I said enthusiastically. "We'll go to the Tayelet. From there, we can see one of the most beautiful panoramas in all of Jerusalem."

The Tayelet walkway on the south side of the city extends for roughly a quarter of a mile. The view was magnificent, as was the aroma of falafel that came from the shops around us. There was no mistaking the distinct Middle East flavor of this dish made from mashed chickpeas fried in oil. I was reminded of the passage in the Talmud that says the aroma of the incense that burned in the ancient Temple permeated the air of Jerusalem to such an extent that it could be smelled throughout the city. Today that scent was falafel.

I noticed as we walked that Jamie was constantly looking over his shoulder. "What are you looking for?" I asked.

"Just checking for terrorists," he said, trying to sound casual. "Aren't you concerned?"

"No," I stopped him abruptly. "I told you, Jamie. You can't live here in constant fear. Besides, this land belongs to the Jewish people. We're not going to allow ourselves to be afraid in our own home. But don't worry about it. You'll get used to it soon."

"Except, of course, when you drive on the roads with these crazy Israeli drivers," Jamie quipped.

Even at that late hour there were all sorts of people walking around, people from many different races, cultures, nationalities, and religions, immigrants from over a hundred and twenty countries, each person with his own special features, unique beauty, and twinkling eyes, each filled with hope and pulsating with energy. These are my people, I thought, from the black Ethiopians to the white British. No matter the superficial differences, we are all Jews, a family.

An Israeli flag waved in the wind at the entrance to the Tayelet. Wherever we went, we could see Israeli flags—in the windows of people's homes, on cars, even in restaurants and car washes. The proud, accomplished nation had paid the ultimate price many times over for the gift of life and freedom. And the people did not take that gift lightly.

"Why are some license plates blue, others red, and some yellow?" Jamie asked, pointing.

"Very perceptive," I reply. "The red license plates are for the police, the yellow are for Israeli drivers, and the blue are for non-Israeli Arab vehicles. You might also notice that on the blue plates is a Hebrew letter, representing the first letter of the city in the West Bank or Gaza in which the Arab-owned car is registered. It's an unfortunate fact of life that such distinguishing markings—a consequence of Israel's war against terrorism—are necessary. It helps the border patrol do their job."

Jamie was full of questions. "And why is it," he asked, "that some of the soldiers' berets are red, others black, and others green? Is it because of where they come from?"

"No. You see," I said, "many of the customs of the Israeli army, and much of Israeli jurisprudence in general, were adopted from the British who governed here before Israel became a state in 1948. The army beret was patterned after the British model. Each group in the Israeli Defense Forces has a different color beret. Red is for paratroopers, blue is for air force, green is for border patrol, black is for the tank corps, and so on."

We finally returned to the hotel after midnight. Though our confused body clocks said it was already morning, we went to sleep for the night.

"*Layla tov*," I said.

"Layla tov," repeated Jamie. He had just learned his first Hebrew expression.

CHAPTER SIX

OUR VISIT TO TANTE RIVKE

Jamie was unprepared for the Israeli breakfast we sat down to the next morning—a huge spread with an array of salads, fish, cheeses, cakes, and breads.

"Let's go someplace different for dinner tonight," Jamie said, digging in with a hearty appetite.

"We're eating breakfast and you're already thinking about where we should have dinner? There is a place in the old city that recreates the decor, ambiance, and even menu of a Roman emporium from the first century. Maybe we'll get to go there one evening."

"How about dancing maidens?" Jamie asked between chews.

"That too. And they give you a toga to put on to add to the experience. They even have a sign for a vomitorium where... well, you can figure out what that is for. Apparently that was a customary ritual after meals in the Roman times."

"They were probably all bulimic," joked Jamie. "Why don't we go tonight?"

"Because I have something unique and even more special in mind for tonight."

The city of Jerusalem was bustling with shoppers on Friday. Everyone was getting ready for the Sabbath.

"Let's go to the Israel museum and see the Dead Sea Scrolls," Jamie said. "That's always fascinated me."

"Sorry, we can't. All public institutions are closed on Friday and Saturday, in reverence for the Moslem and Jewish Sabbath." Jamie looked a bit disappointed.

"I have a better idea." I said. "Let's go to the *shuk*. You haven't been to Israel until you've gone to the *shuk*."

Before he could ask, I explained. "A *shuk* is a marketplace where they sell vegetables, fruit, challah, which is the Sabbath bread, and other such items. It's like a flea market filled with food, with hundreds of people shopping in the narrow aisles."

We walked to *Mahaneh Yehuda*, the main *shuk* in Jerusalem, and casually strolled through the aisles. Suddenly we heard someone shout, "*Shel me hatik?*" Whose bag is this? A near panic erupted in the crowd of shoppers before it was determined that the suspicious object only belonged to a little boy, by that time in tears, who had put down his lunch bag and walked a few steps away to look at a candy display.

יהוה

Wherever one goes in Israel, one will see this sign: BE ALERT FOR SUSPICIOUS OBJECTS. One will also notice something called a *bor bitachon,* a security hole, a small steel-reenforced pit where suspicious objects can be placed. Israelis are thoroughly habituated to be on the alert for bombs and terrorist attacks. Volunteer squads of teenage youth who are too young to serve in the army routinely walk through the streets and buses checking for hidden bombs. Thankfully, the spirit of volunteerism is still strong among much of Israeli youth.

The open and undefended *shuk* is a natural target for suicide bombers who can cause horrible carnage with just one bomb, especially on Friday when it is packed with Sabbath shoppers. As a result of the terrorist attacks in the past, many Israelis have stopped shopping in the Arab *shuk* in Eastern Jerusalem, and most are more alert and on their guard in the Jewish *shuk* as well.

The entire relationship between Jews and Arabs has changed drastically since the intifada. The liberal vision of peace that guided the prior generation of Israelis—that some day Arabs and Jews, biblical cousins, would learn to live together on the same land—has given way to a call for separation between the two peoples. At the core of the conflict is a clash between two systems of justice, and ultimately a resolution of the Arab-Israeli conflict will not come about until both sides acknowledge that neither has exclusive possession of the truth. But will a true peace ever be found? Or must the messiah come before peace is ushered in?

יְהוָה

We sat down for lunch in a small café, and Ehud Olmert, the charismatic mayor of Jerusalem, walked in wearing a T-shirt and blue jeans.

"Isn't that the mayor?" Jamie asked, aghast.

"Yes," I said. "The politicians here in Israel are very informal."

"Hello, Rabbi," he said to me, clasping my shoulder warmly. We schmoozed for a while, careful to steer our conversation away from politics. We talked instead of how magnificent the city of Jerusalem is and on weighty matters such as whether the falafel at this café is better than at the restaurant down the block. Ehud was excited about the series of feature articles Jamie was writing for the magazine and cordially offered his help.

Jerusalem pretty much comes to a complete halt on Friday at sundown with the beginning of *Shabbat*. Last to close are the flower shops. Israelis love flowers, and almost everyone takes a bouquet home for the *Shabbat* table. I bought a small bouquet and said to Jamie, "This is for my *Tante Rivka,* which is Yiddish for Aunt Rebecca, an elderly relative of mine I haven't seen for two years. If you don't mind, I'd like to visit her before *Shabbat*."

We walked a few blocks to her tiny apartment in a modest neighborhood. I knocked on her door. *Tante Rivka* opened the door quickly without even asking who was there. She recognized me instantly. It was a bit awkward greeting her. My female relatives are very religious and do not allow men to hug them, even close friends and family. I introduced her to Jamie, and she offered us a cup of tea. As we schmoozed, I was reminded of the fact that Arabs and Israelis share this same Middle Eastern characteristic of showing hospitality to visitors. *Tante Rivka* entertained us by telling me stories about my late grandfather, her brother, and what a mischievous troublemaker he was as a child.

Almost every Jew today has a relative living in Israel. That's because most Jews in America came from Eastern Europe, particularly Russia, and had ancestors who came to the U.S. between 1880 and 1920. Most of their relatives who remained in Europe were killed in the Holocaust. After the war, the survivors came to the one nation that would take them, Israel.

Tante Rivka was a widow and lived alone in a tiny flat in the ultra Orthodox neighborhood of *Meah Shearim*. She led a simple, spartan life, and always insisted she was happy and content. Her apartment was filled, wall to wall, with

Jewish books, and her every sentence was peppered with the phrase *baruch Hashem.* Thank God. Although a truism, I am reminded of how the happiest people in life are often those with the least money and material possessions. She told me how fortunate she was and how grateful to God that she was "rich," and then she quoted from the Talmud in the Ethics of the Fathers: "Who is a wealthy person? He who is happy with his lot."

"I have all I need, *baruch Hashem,* unlike Chavale next door, a mother of eight children, trying to marry off six daughters and take care of her sons. Now *she* needs help."

Although tiny, her apartment was orderly and immaculate. I remembered visiting Tante Rivka with my own little children ten years earlier and how shaken they were by the experience, having never before been exposed to such modest living arrangements. I asked her in Hebrew if there was anything she needed.

"What could I possibly need?" she answered, her eyes twinkling and a big smile crossing her face. And then, quoting from the *Torah,* she continued. "I'm like Abraham who said, 'I have everything.'" She chuckled. "He probably got that line from Sarah."

"A feminist?" I asked, teasing her a bit.

"*Vos iz dos?*" What is that? she asked, reverting to her *mama lashon,* mother tongue, of Yiddish.

I decided not to push it.

For ten minutes, Tante Rivka kept talking about "my boys." For a while, I thought she was referring to her four sons, until it became clear she was talking about the young men who go to the army. All the soldiers in the Israeli army were "her boys."

As we were chatting, Jamie noticed that the front door was open. As he rose to shut it, Tante Rivka jumped out of her chair and held it open, chastising him in Yiddish.

"What's she saying? What did I do?" Jamie asked, recoiling and sliding back into his seat.

I explained that there is a Jewish law prohibiting men from being alone in a room with a woman who is not their wife. This is to prevent any fraternizing or sexual misconduct, though I doubt the law was intended for our situation of being alone with my eighty-year-old great aunt. But I deeply respected the fact that this was how she had led her entire life, putting fences around the law and keeping as far away from sin as possible. Besides, I got a kick out of hearing her get all excited in Yiddish.

As I stood up to leave, I gave her a hundred-dollar bill. Tante Rivka was speechless. Quickly regaining her composure, she bolted out the door screaming, "Chavale, you're not going to believe what my nephew brought you." Sensing my dismay that she wasn't keeping the money herself, she turned to me and said, "You think you're the only one entitled to do the *mitzvah* of giving *tzedakah?*" Charity?

As we walked out of her small apartment after saying good-bye, I turned to Jamie and smiled in pride. Tante Rivka was the kind of Jew I was so proud of. This was what I wanted to show Jamie, not the spiritually-bereft, materialistic tycoon many non-Jews conjure up in their mind when they think of Jews. I wanted to show him the humble old woman with hardly any material possessions, who was deeply satisfied with her lot, and who shared her widow's mite, the meager bit she had, with the less fortunate.

After we said our farewells, we made our way back to the hotel. On the way, Jamie pointed to a little girl playing and calling out to her friend in Hebrew.

"What's she saying?" Jamie asked.

"She's saying, 'throw me the ball,'" I interpreted for him.

"That's amazing how well they speak Hebrew," Jamie said. "It must be heartwarming for you to hear children speaking Hebrew so naturally, not only to convey religious ideas but for mundane purposes like 'pass me the ball.'"

He couldn't have been more right. He was beginning to see a little from my perspective, and it delighted me. "It is, indeed! It is the only such instance in human history in which a language was resurrected after two thousand years of disuse to become the commonly spoken one it is today. Hebrew is alive and well in the Promised Land."

"Abraham and Sarah would have been proud," said Jamie.

We walked deeper into the *Meah Shearim* neighborhood, and I began to feel overwhelmed by the preponderance of men with long beards, black robes, and side curls, and women with long skirts and hair coverings pushing strollers.

"I must admit," I said, "that even to me, they seem so antiquated and even strange, a curiosity and relic from the past."

"And you come from a Hassidic family and background!" declared Jamie, implying how peculiar the sights must seem to him with no cultural or religious ties to Jews.

As I wondered what Jamie was thinking of these people, I was struck by a frightening thought. What if my grandparents had not come to America in 1929? That would have been me out there wearing that long black robe and hat and sweltering in the hot sun! And then I asked myself, could my grandparents have been wrong in leaving Israel for America and shedding their distinctive garb and culture on the boat over in order to fit into their new surroundings? What might my life have been like had they stayed in Jerusalem? Would I have been happier and more fulfilled as a Hassid? I was haunted by the question of what price I was paying for modernity and for living in America. And was that cost too high?

"Why do so many women wear berets?" Jamie asked. "Because of the British system?"

"Interesting observation, Jamie," I responded. "No. Actually, most married Orthodox women, for reasons of modesty, cover their hair with a hat, scarf, or stylish beret and remove it only when alone with their family. Here in this fundamentalist Haredi Orthodox neighborhood, the women also wear long skirts with long sleeves and even socks. And do you see all those signs posted on building walls throughout the neighborhood?"

"I noticed them right away," said Jamie. "I assumed they are advertisements for the local stores' products."

"Not at all," I said. "They're signs warning visitors to dress as modestly as the *Torah* commands."

"This is all still liberal compared to the way women in fundamentalist Muslim countries like Iran and Afghanistan have to dress," said Jamie. "There, as you know, they have to cover their faces, not just their hair, and wear long, form-less black robes, nothing like the colorful and stylish clothes these Orthodox Jewish women are wearing. But I guess they all have one thing in common. In one way or another, they are declaring for all to hear: 'I am an ultra religious woman.'"

So that's what Jamie thought of these people I loved and who represented my own family roots. He saw them scorn-fully like the fundamentalist zealots of Iran and Afghanistan or, perhaps if he were generous, quaintly like the Amish. And what did Jamie think of me, also an Orthodox Jew, albeit a more modern one, who dressed the same way any other American did, save for the yarmulke on my head? I was resigned to the notion that on one level or another he probably saw us all as somehow foreign, differ-ent, and "other," the same way I viewed the Amish, Iranians, and Afghans. But that seemed so unfair.

To me, the Hassidim were real people whom I knew and cared for, and whose lifestyle and faith I deeply respected. I wondered, was I expecting too much of Jamie? Furthermore, were I to come to know the Amish and Iranian people the way I know Hassidim—not in a detached way from the outside but from the inside—might my views of them change for the positive? In other words, does greater knowledge of a foreign group and more contact with them breed deeper fellowship and caring, or does it breed their opposites—contempt and enmity?

I interrupted my musings by asking myself whether I was judging people, again, by superficial characteristics like the clothes they wore. Was I assuming positive views of them if they were Jews whose culture I was familiar with and with whom I felt a kinship? And negative views if they were foreign to me and not "my people"?

"You know, Rabbi," Jamie said, "You Jewish people somehow feel united by your collective past. Despite your racial, cultural, political, and religious diversity, Jews are bonded together as a community in the finest sense of the term. I stand in awe at how you care for one another—for the Soviet Jews, black Ethiopians, people you don't know and have never met. That's admirable."

Jamie was right. This was one of our greatest strengths and sources of pride, our unity as a people.

"But you have that in your Christian tradition too, Jamie," I said reassuringly. "The duty to feel one with 'the body of Christ.'" I knew I was right theologically. But I also knew that both Protestants and Catholics are weaker in carrying out their ideal in practice than are Jews.

We came to the center of the neighborhood square, where a Hassid with a long black coat, hat, and beard was stopping men who were not dressed like him and urging them to put on phylacteries.

"Are you Jewish?" he asked me.

"Yes," I replied to the Hassid.

"Did you put on tefillin this morning as the *Torah* commands?" he asked.

"Yes, I did," I responded, quickly proving my *bona fides* by citing the commandment in Hebrew, "And you shall bind them as a sign on your hand and as frontlets between your eyes." He smiled and turned his attention to someone else, no doubt assuming that Jamie was Jewish and had put on tefillin that day too.

"That's noble," said Jamie.

"What is 'noble'?" I asked.

"That he feels so strongly about his faith that he stands outside in the hot sun sharing it with others."

"You're right, Jamie," I agreed. "But in that respect he's like the evangelists in your own tradition who endure all sorts of difficulties and even indignities to share the gospel with others, all because they believe so deeply in it."

"You know something," Jamie said reflectively, "I'm here for just a few days, and already I realize that a trip to Israel is a heavy-duty affair for us Christians. What I don't understand is how you Jews from the diaspora feel living outside Israel. Don't you feel like you're missing the boat of history? Even guilty for not living here? I can't comprehend, given the significance of the Holy Land to the Jewish faith, why American and European Jews would not run to move here, not just visit."

It had come to that—being admonished by this non-Jewish reporter I just met a few days ago for not being Jewish and Zionist enough! How dare he be so judgmental?

And how dare he touch such a sensitive chord with his simple, penetrating question.

Then again, that's what happens here in Israel to Jews and Christians alike. Like a potent truth serum, Jerusalem has a unique way of going to the heart of people's convictions and bringing to the surface their rawest, deepest emotions. There's no being blasé here. It's an all-or-nothing atmosphere that elicits one's true, unpretentious inner self.

CHAPTER SEVEN
THE WALL

We returned to our hotel and began preparing for the *Shabbat*. "What better way for us to welcome the Sabbath than by going to prayer services at the *Kotel Hamaaravi*, the Western Wall?" I said.

"Is that the same as the Wailing Wall?" Jamie asked, interested.

"Yes, only we don't call it that, Jamie. The Kotel, as we refer to it, is the only remaining wall from the Second Temple, which was destroyed in 70 C.E. For us Jews, the Kotel is the center of the universe, the holiest place on earth."

"Then why do I know it as the Wailing Wall?" Jamie asked, confused.

"Because for centuries, Jamie, Jews cried there over the destruction of the Temple and exile of the Jewish people from the land. As a result, non-Jews began referring to it as the Wailing Wall."

Undoubtedly, the most poignant moment of the 1967 Six Day War was when the Wall was liberated. Every Jew alive today and old enough to remember that war still has inscribed indelibly in his mind the image captured in the famous photograph of the brave conquering paratroopers praying and crying over the liberation of the Wall. Jews take pride in the fact that, instead of celebrating their victory by going to bars and getting drunk, Israeli soldiers came to the Wall to pray to God.

יהוה

Ideally, Jews are to *daven*, meaning pray, in a synagogue with a *minyan,* a quorum of ten men or more. Such is the importance of peoplehood and community in Judaism. Reform and Conservative Judaism count women to the minyan, as well. When there is a minyan, Jews recite the central prayer of the service, the *shmoneh esray*, twice, first silently and alone, and then the cantor repeats it out loud. If this is not possible, we are to *daven* alone, even it it is not in a synagogue.

The Jewish liturgy is unusual in that it is almost entirely in the collective form—"heal us," "save us," "forgive us," and so on. This is a powerful, central motif in Judaism, and is quite different from the Christian prayer experience that is far more individualistic and existential in nature.

In Judaism, we approach God by first looking inward to ourselves, then horizontally by reflecting on the world, mankind, and the Jewish people, and only then by connecting vertically to God. To paraphrase the New Testament in a Jewish way, "There is no coming to the Father except through his sons and daughters and his world." This same dichotomy underlies the fundamental distinction between Jewish prayers for redemption, which are communal in nature, and Christian prayers for salvation, which are individualistic.

To be sure, the differences are in degree not kind. For Jewish prayer is also concerned with the individual's actions and personal relationship with God, while Christian prayers, of course, seek to extend salvation to the whole world. And yet, the fundamental orientations, revolving around the question of what is one's starting point in life, essentially differ. For the Jew, it is the question, "What have we done to redeem *the world* and make it a better place?" For Christians, on the other hand, it is the Augustinian question of, "Are *you* saved?"

יְהוָה

"Let's hurry, Jamie," I said, coming back from my reverie. "The *Shabbat* begins in just twenty minutes."

We hopped in a cab and were dropped off outside the large promenade in front of the Wall ten minutes later. Archeological excavations continue in the area of the Wall, with something new being discovered almost every day.

"One of the most amazing things, Jamie," I said as we walked toward the promenade, "is that there are always people praying at the Kotel any time of the day or night. Wherever in the world Jews live, they pray facing the Kotel, the last extant wall that encircled the *Har Habayit,* the Temple Mount of Jerusalem. In America, Jews face east; in Russia, south; in the northern part of Israel, south; in the southern part of Israel, north, and so on. In Jerusalem itself, we pray facing the Kotel and Har Habayit."

Jamie looked somewhat puzzled. "Doesn't the Jewish tradition say the Temple was also built on Mount Moriah, where Abraham was going to sacrifice his son, Isaac?" he asked.

I was dumbfounded by his astute insight.

"How did you know that?" I asked as we turned the corner and could see the edge of the Kotel.

Jamie was silent. I'm not sure if he heard me. He was deep in thought...or else sleepwalking!

As in all public places—movie theaters, department stores, and even synagogues—we had to pass through a security check. You get used to such inconveniences after a while, just as we in America have become accustomed to screenings in airports and government buildings. Not surprisingly, Israelis are far more vigilant against terrorism than we in the States are... thank God for that.

No matter how many times I had visited the Kotel, I still felt a profound sense of awe when it came into view. I approached the Wall slowly and kissed its cold stones. Tears of joy and thanksgiving to God, for granting me the privilege of returning to this holy place, flowed down my cheeks. I prayed, as I had done repeatedly in the past, that I would return here, once again, to this Wall, my spiritual epicenter.

I recited my afternoon *Mincha* prayers and was elevated to a spiritual high—religious endorphins, I call them—that I rarely achieve in the States. I took out a list of people from my pocket, mostly Christians, who had sent me their prayer requests and asked me to pray for them at the Wall. I was deeply moved by those who had sent me their prayers, and by the heartfelt and inspiring prayers. Some asked me to beseech God for divine healing for their families or themselves, some for a better job, others for more income, still others for better relations with their children or spouse. Those who asked me to pray that God would bless Jerusalem with peace touched me especially.

Just as they had requested, I prayed for these people—hundreds of them—at this holiest of sites. And I felt privileged to do so. But I also felt inadequate to the task and humbled that these good people, Christians as well as Jews, entrusted me with such a profound mission.

I noticed, out of the corner of my eye, that Jamie was writing a note and placing it in the cracks of the Wall. He, a Christian, was as moved as I was by touching the hem of God's holy earthly garments.

"What did you pray for?" I asked reverently.

"I asked that God would restore my faith in him." Jamie looked abashed, humbled.

Our hearts were filled with awe, humility, and thanksgiving. "Thank you, God," I prayed aloud, "for giving of your Spirit to mankind and for enabling us to feel your presence so powerfully in our lives."

Walking away from the wall, I decided the time was ripe to share with Jamie an ancient Jewish commentary on the *Torah*. "Do you, Jamie, by chance, remember the biblical verse, 'And you shall build for me a *Temple* and I will dwell *in them*'? The rabbis point out that the last word of the verse, in Hebrew *b'tocham,* should have been in the singular, 'and I [God] will dwell in *it*," meaning the Temple. Why does it say the plural 'in them'? The rabbis explain that the *Torah* wishes to teach us that the ultimate importance of the Temple is not its edifice, but how it affects the hearts of the people, that is, 'them.' For as the prophet said, 'Will God's presence fill a house? His glory is throughout the world.' The real significance of the Temple is that it enhances God's presence among the people, by making them mindful of Him always."

"That's interesting," said Jamie, "though I doubt the switch from singular to plural was deliberate on the part of the scribe and divinely ordained, and was not simply a scribal error at some historical juncture. But it's a nice commentary. I like it," he said, nodding. "And I can certainly understand how it was meaningful and instructive to Jews over the centuries."

"Well," I said, "now is not the time to debate Welhaussen's theory of biblical criticism, Jamie. But I do have another interesting Talmudic explanation to share with you since you liked the first one so much. According to the rabbis, the two ancient Jewish temples were destroyed as a punishment for senseless hatred among the Jewish people themselves. On this, the late Chief Rabbi of Israel, Rav Kook, offered a wonderful addendum. If the temple was destroyed because of the sin of senseless *hatred* among brothers, he said, it will, one day, be rebuilt when we extend senseless *love* toward our brothers."

"Hey!" said Jamie, "I'll bet that's what Jesus was alluding to when he said that the third temple would come from *heaven*. Maybe what he meant was it would be built with the *help* of heaven, in other words, when people would bring heaven down to earth and extend agape or love toward one another."

"That's an apt interpretation," I responded. "Look at the two of us, Jamie, Jew and Christian, here at the Wall, sharing interpretations of our scriptures with one another, engaging in a dialogue."

"And resonating with each other's words too," Jamie said. "Maybe you'll become a Christian yet, Rabbi," he continued with a grin.

"True dialogue is being open to the journey and the ideas one encounters along that journey," I said.

"Okay," said Jamie. "I'll be honest with you. I know the Temple was central for Judaism because it was the site where Jews brought sacrifices and prayed to God. But the idea of killing all those animals seems terribly barbaric and even pagan to me."

"The institution of sacrifices is, unfortunately, often misunderstood by outsiders," I said. "Almost all of the animal sacrifices were eaten by the priests or those who brought them. They were a way in which the people demonstrated their love for God and came closer to him. Even the Hebrew word for sacrifice, *korban,* comes from the root 'to come closer.' The sacrifice imbued the mundane act of eating with holiness and meaning. It also served as a powerful force for democratizing life, since everyone was able to bring them, though the poor only had to bring what they could afford."

A glint of recognition lit up Jamie's eye. "Maybe that's why," he said, "the Bible stresses that the true value of sacrifices is not in its cost, but in the degree to which the one bringing it gives it from the heart."

"Excellent point," I add. "I see your childhood Sunday-school lessons stayed with you. We, indeed, find phrases repeated like 'each person according to his ability,' or 'a man who brings *from himself* a sacrifice.' You're absolutely correct, Jamie. The *Torah* is stressing not so much the obligation of bringing a sacrifice, but the fact that it should be brought volitionally, from one's inner will and intent, not out of duty."

"That's honestly one of the problems I have with Judaism," said Jamie. "The fact that you're obligated to pray three times a day, with set prayers on top of that. Doesn't it take away from the spontaneity and feeling of the ritual?"

Jamie had put his finger on a real problem. For most Jews in most synagogues, prayer services are boring social gatherings, not uplifting spiritual ones. But that discussion was not for now. Instead, I decided to continue focusing on the moral lessons derived from the biblical commentaries.

"That is also, Jamie, why the *Torah* stresses the idea that 'a poor *soul* brings an offering,' since the poor man, in bringing his widow's mite, is really bringing his soul. This is the true meaning of sacrifices and, similarly, of prayer today, which has replaced animal sacrifices, since we are biblically proscribed from offering sacrifices outside the Temple.

"The important thing to remember, Jamie," I continued, "is that God does not need our sacrifices. *We* need them. This is what Jeremiah so forcefully meant when he declared: '"What need have I of all your sacrifices?" Says the LORD. "I am sated with burnt offerings of rams."' Rather, the essential message of Judaism is that through our sacrifices and prayers, we can come closer to God and express our soul's longing to cling to Him.

"Hey," said Jamie, teasing me, "that's persuasive. You could be a preacher!"

The Kotel is not only the repository of the two-thousand-year-old Jewish dream of the ingathering of the exiles. On Friday night it is also the ultimate Jewish meeting place. That evening, I met my old college roommate, a former teacher, and a Christian who recognized me from when I spoke several years earlier at her Assembly of God church in Oklahoma City.

As Jamie and I turned to leave following the *Maariv* evening services, Jamie said, "Let me take a picture of us here together by the Wall. It'll be a great shot to accompany my story."

"No!" I screamed in panic. "You can't take pictures on the *Shabbat*. A camera works with batteries, and that is regarded as a form of fire. It's true that Reform and Conservative Jews use electricity on *Shabbat* since they do not view batteries as a form of fire included in the biblical prohibition that 'You shall not light a *fire* on the Sabbath day.' But the Orthodox disagree."

I realized two things at that moment—first, how absolutely antiquated and absurd this prohibition must seem to outsiders like Jamie; second, how hysterical my instinctive response must have seemed to him. But religious bystanders probably would have attacked poor Jamie had he publicly desecrated the Sabbath, even innocently, at this holy site.

Jamie was a bit shaken by the intensity of my response.

"Sor-r-ry," he said with feigned sincerity. "Just trying to do my job and capture the moment."

Before I could say anything more, Jamie turned to a man nearby and said, "Do you have change for a ten-shekel coin?"

The man, wearing a big black hat and beard, looked at him like he was crazy and walked off.

"Boy, that guy was certainly unfriendly," said Jamie.

"No," I said, explaining, "just observant. We are not permitted to touch money on the Sabbath, either. He probably thought you were taunting him."

"I certainly didn't mean to offend him," Jamie said, his feathers a bit ruffled.

יהוה

This time, I was more patient with him. After all, how could he know about these seemingly minor Sabbath infractions? And yet, I noted, we tend to judge others, and even reprimand them as I did, when ignorance is at fault, not maliciousness. We rarely understand the culture and religious sensitivities of other people who are different from us. I am convinced that if we don't understand others—who they are and what makes them tick—we cannot demonstrate courteous sensitivity to them. Inevitably we will offend them in some way.

I am also convinced that we tend to notice, and look disparagingly toward, peculiarities in other traditions that can often be found, albeit in a different form, in our own. This became clear to me years earlier when I had dinner with the president of the Southern Baptist Convention following his infamous statement that "God Almighty does not hear the prayers of Jews."

During our dinner together, he complimented the waiter on the delicious dessert.

"What is it?" he asked, biting into his third piece.

"Rum balls," said the waiter.

The Baptist pastor's mouth dropped mid sentence. Aghast, he spit out what was in his mouth.

"It's just a rum ball," I said, reassuringly.

"Yes, but what would my congregation think of me if they saw me eating rum balls, which contain liquor, and with a rabbi! Imagine if you were seen by members of your synagogue eating pork with me!"

יְהֹוָה

"Let's hop in a cab back to the hotel and eat dinner," Jamie said as we made our way past the throngs of worshipers leaving the Wall. "Oops, I forgot. We can't ride in a car on the Sabbath. Right? It's a form of work because the engine's combustion creates a fire."

"Very good," I said. "You could be a rabbi soon at the rate you're going. Go ahead, you take a cab. I'll walk and meet you there."

"No way," Jamie said, "I love seeing how extreme you Orthodox are. Just one question," he persisted. "I understand why you can't drive a car on *Shabbat*. But what's wrong with riding in one if someone else is driving it? Besides, I've been working with Jews at the magazine in New York for years, and every one of them drives on the Sabbath."

"I guess they're not Orthodox," I said, deliberately avoiding his first question, which was actually an incisive one that would have been too complex for quick response at that moment. It also would have involved a fair amount of Talmudic casuistry.

I was so caught up in our conversation, I wasn't paying attention to where we were going. Apparently, we made a wrong turn leaving the Wall and found ourselves lost and alone, surrounded by darkness, in the heart of the Arab quarter. Not a desirable place for a Jew to be, by any means.

"The city of Jerusalem has, for hundreds of years, been divided into quarters—Jewish, Armenian, Arab, and Christian," I began to explain calmly.

Wisdom prevailing, Jamie said, "Forget the history—let's get the heck out of here." Which we did, walking briskly.

When we reached our hotel, Christian tourists getting ready to go out to dinner filled the lobby.

"I'm going up to the room to freshen up a bit before dinner," Jamie said.

"Okay. I'll meet you downstairs in fifteen minutes."

I arrived back in the lobby on time. Jamie came down ten minutes later looking exasperated and hardly refreshed.

"Why are you so late?" I asked.

"You've got a strange elevator system here," he muttered. "I can't believe it stopped on every floor and waited for ten seconds each time, all the way from the nineteenth floor down."

"Oh," I chuckled, "you must have gotten on the *Shabbat* elevator."

"What's the *Shabbat* elevator?" Jamie asked impatiently. "And why does it hate Christians?"

"As you know, Jamie, we're not allowed to use electricity on *Shabbat*. So most hotels in Israel have at least one elevator bank set aside to accommodate Orthodox Jews. It stops automatically on every floor so we don't have to press the button and make it go."

"Strange people, these Jews," he mumbled under his breath.

Actually, I agreed. From the outside, the elevator modification does seem like carrying the law to an almost bizarre degree. That's probably why Christians resonate so well with Jesus' attacks on the Pharisees for their excessive legalism and concern for the minutiae of the law. And yet, from within, the Orthodox *Weltanschauung* and belief system maintain that the law is observed only out of our desire to be fully obedient to God's word and to come closer to him. Far from a burden, our obsessiveness with ritual and legal detail is seen as an act of love for God. We are not to abandon the trees for the forest, nor the reverse.

"If anything, Jamie," I said, "the burden is on you Christians to explain why you do *not* observe many of the laws of the *Torah* today. A couple of prohibitions would be lighting a fire on *Shabbat* and wearing a garment made from wool and linen. And there are the commandments to wear a prayer shawl and phylacteries. After all, how do you Christians, who view the Bible as the inerrant and divine word of God, distinguish between ethical commandments like 'love thy neighbor as thyself,' which you insist remains authoritative, and ritual ones like 'you shall not light a fire on Sabbath,' which you claim are not?"

"Okay," said Jamie, "I admit that's a fair question. But don't try to tell me that all those intricate Jewish laws were around during Jesus' time, let alone that they are divine and date from Moses and Sinai. That's why Jesus often attacked the Pharisees for being hypocritical and overly legalistic. Besides I doubt even non-Orthodox Jews agree with you on this matter."

"You're right, they don't," I answered. "But let me explain a few basic things. All forms of Judaism today–and that means Reform and Conservative, as well as Orthodox—agree that they originated in the Pharisaic movement of the first century, the very group so maligned in the New Testament. The institution of the synagogue, the authority of the rabbis, even the validity of prayer apart from sacrifices—all were Pharisaic innovations current in Jesus' time.

"And while there were, undoubtedly, some segments of the Pharisees that were as hypocritical and legalistic as Christians maintain—and even the Talmud admits as much—most were not. In fact, most Bible scholars today believe that Jesus, as well as Paul, were Pharisees. For it was precisely because Jesus and Paul cared most about Pharisaic Jews and Judaism and felt that they were part of that faith community that they reproved and castigated it as they did. People don't try to correct a system that is totally alien to them and which they have no common basis with or interest in. Instead, they focus on those with which they share common beliefs."

"I accept that," said Jamie patiently.

"Well," I continued, "over the centuries, many rabbinic laws were added to prevent us from coming to violate the core biblical laws themselves. These are called the 'fences' around the law which can, indeed, become both numerous and cumbersome. But Orthodox Jews adhere to them, nonetheless, in the belief that they, too, are somehow divinely ordained. We observe them out of love and obedience to God's calling on us."

"That explains much better," said Jamie, "why you observe the law with the meticulousness you do."

"And the laws of the *Shabbat* are perhaps the most numerous and intricate, yet the most curiously beloved. For they create for us the context in which we can isolate the Sabbath day and celebrate it to the fullest. In fact, the noted nineteenth-century Jewish poet Ahad Haam once wrote, 'more than Israel has preserved the Sabbath, the Sabbath has preserved Israel.'

"The Sabbath is also the most difficult time to be away from one's family," I added. "That's why I make it my business, with rare exceptions, to be home on *Shabbat*. For in Judaism, the family more than the synagogue is at the center of Jewish life and serves as the key to Jewish survival and continuity. These two institutions, the family and the *Shabbat*, are the primary repositories of our Jewish heritage and are the principal agents for transmitting Jewish faith and values to the next generation. The family reaches its most profound state of harmony and love at the Friday night supper and Saturday lunch. I often wonder how people who do not observe the Sabbath manage to keep their families together. I also wonder how people without a family are able to truly experience the full beauty of the *Shabbat*."

Being in Jerusalem for Sabbath with Jamie led me to wonder whether he felt as incomplete in his bachelor status as I felt lonely without my family. I decided it was too touchy and intimate a question to ask my new friend.

We walked into the dining room and sat down at our pre-assigned table. Jamie was, by that time, really getting into the program. He was performing the various Sabbath rituals with me, humming along as I sang the song welcoming the Sabbath angels to our home, and even reciting—in English, of course—the passage from Proverbs: "What a rare find is a capable wife...," extolling my wife, in absentia. "That's really nice," Jamie said. "Do you recite that every time you're away from your wife?"

"No," I chuckled. "The husband chants this every Friday night before sitting down to eat the Sabbath meal."

"Then what?" Jamie asked.

"Then we bless our children with the biblical blessing. We place our hands over their bowed heads and, for girls, begin with 'may you be like Sarah, Rebecca, Rachel, and Leah,' and for boys, 'may you be like Ephraim and Menashe.' We continue, 'May the lord bless you, may he always watch over you, may he let his light shine upon you and be gracious unto you. May he lift up his countenance onto you and grant you peace.' Now you know why I miss my family so much on *Shabbat* when I'm away. The whole Sabbath setting is structured around it."

"I know what you're trying to do," said Jamie slyly. "I see right through you. You're trying to get me envious so I'll marry a Jewish girl, convert to Judaism, and have a family of my own. Why don't you just hire one of your famous Jewish matchmakers?"

With that, to my absolute horror, Jamie stood up in the middle of the dining room and began singing at the top of his lungs the matchmaker song from *Fiddler on the Roof*. His dining-room audience clapped and roared with laughter.

"Can we eat now?" Jamie said, sitting down nonchalantly, but clearly energized by the attention he had received.

I decided now was hardly the time to explain to him the Jewish position that not only do we not attempt to convert non-Jews, but we also try to discourage them from becoming Jews.

"We can't eat quite yet, Jamie. We must first say the *kiddush*, the sanctification over the wine."

We rose and I recited the kiddush, mainly verses from Genesis describing the Sabbath as a symbol of creation, a day of holiness, and a reminder of our exodus from Egypt. I drank some of the wine and passed the cup to Jamie.

"Ah, alcohol, finally, for the goy! I hope our guy from the Board of Health isn't on duty tonight." Drinking the whole cup, he said, "Now can we eat?"

"Soon. First, come with me."

We walked into the kitchen to wash our hands ritually and returned to our table where I made the traditional blessing over two loaves of bread: "Blessed art thou lord, our God, king of the universe, who brings forth this bread from the earth."

"Why two loaves?" he asked. "One for you and one for me?"

"No," I explained patiently. "On Sabbath, we take two loaves as a reminder of our forefathers' experience in the desert. Just as they collected a double portion of manna on Friday, keeping one portion for Saturday when they were not permitted to collect food, so we are not to work or want for anything, even food, but to have everything prepared in advance.

"That's nice," he said humoring me. "*Now* can we eat?"

"Yes, Jamie," I said in a correspondingly pedantic tone, "now we can eat."

And eat we did. During the meal, I explained how it is customary to eat more on the Sabbath than during the rest of the week, how we are to enjoy good food, fine clothing, and even to engage in sexual relations with our spouse on the Sabbath. There is nothing ascetic about this religion. Judaism affirms pleasure and materialism, though it insists they be elevated and sanctified—food through blessing, sexuality through marriage, money through charity, and so on. In Judaism, the highest level of holiness is to engage the world in its carnality and imbue it with spirituality, not to evade it or detach ourselves from it.

"I remember reading about that in college," Jamie said, stuffing his mouth with chopped liver. "But how do you deal with the basic conflict or dichotomy between the physical and spiritual worlds? In other words, how could the world, which is physical and corporeal, have emanated from a God who is pure spirit?"

"Great question," I answered, a bit taken aback by his erudition. "The ancient Jewish kabbalists, representing the more mystical side of Judaism, explained it this way: Since God is omnipresent, He voluntarily restrained himself by pulling back, an act of *tzimtzum*. In the void that was left, the material world was created. But there still remained sparks of his holiness or *nitzozot* in that material world. The human task is to find and affirm those divine sparks inherent in all creation and to elevate them. For as the Bible teaches, after each day of creation God said it was 'good.' We are to redeem or fix the world—*tikun olam*—by affirming the inherent goodness of the world, capturing the sparks of holiness in all creation, including man, and sanctifying our lives so they give witness to that holiness. Man plays a central role as partner with God in redeeming or fixing the world.

"This is one reason Jews the world over are so involved in social justice causes, from ensuring civil rights to saving the whales. At the core of the Jewish mission is our duty to redeem the world. The notion of the fall of man and his being shackled by sinfulness, unable to rise to the level of partner with God without grace—so central a theme in Christianity—plays little, if any, role in Jewish thinking. To be sure, man's power can be abused and directed to evil rather than to creativity and holiness. That is one reason we celebrate the *Shabbat*. For through the *Shabbat*, we cease creating in this material world for one day a week and remember the true Creator who gave us the power, ability, and authority to create the rest of the week long.

"Well," I said, concluding my spiel, "now you know Jewish Mysticism 101."

"Hold it," said Jamie, staring at the piping hot chicken soup before him. "If electricity is prohibited on *Shabbat*, how do they cook our food?" His tone reflected more of a gotcha attitude than one of genuine inquiry.

"Good question," I affirmed. "Actually, the food was cooked before Sabbath and kept warm on the stove, which remains lit on a low flame throughout the *Shabbat*."

"That explains why everything is so dry," he quipped. "Seriously," he asked, "is this what a Sabbath meal was like in Jesus' time?"

"Essentially," I said, "but I wouldn't say 'Jesus' too loudly here."

"Why not?" Jamie asked.

"Because he's not a very popular man in Jewish circles. Many, if not most, Jews blame him for anti-Semitism."

"But Jesus was a Jew who preached love and tolerance toward others. Why is he blamed for what his followers did in his name?" Jamie asked.

"You're right, Jamie, he shouldn't be. But the fact is that most Jews' views of Jesus are intertwined with their predominantly negative views of Christians who persecuted them over the centuries. Their attitudes toward Jesus and Christianity are shaped by the kind of interaction they or their ancestors have had with the presenters of the Christian faith—the better the relationship, the more positive the Jews' views.

"I admit," I continued, "that today many Jews are, themselves, prejudiced and intolerant toward Christians. I am convinced that the way to fight such biases is to facilitate more positive interaction between the two faith communities. This way neither would stereotype the other, but instead each would come to see the other for the people they truly are, not as ignorant preconception would have them be. But we are far from achieving this goal. Even Christians who seek to help the Jewish people are often rebuffed, their overtures spurned by Jews who remain suspicious of such assistance. While Israelis are less guilty of this than American Jews, most Jews still have a tough time believing there are Christians out there who love them, without ulterior motives, as many insist they do, and who genuinely seek to stand in solidarity with them at their time of need."

יהוה

We finished dessert and left the dining room. Someone in the hall greeted us with the traditional Sabbath greeting, "*Shabbat shalom.*" May you have a peaceful Sabbath. Another said simply, "*Gut Shabbes,*" a Yiddish phrase meaning "Have a good Sabbath." Jamie smiled warmly and responded in kind, "*Shabbat shalom.*"

CHAPTER EIGHT
THE HASSIDIC TISCH

"Now I have the special surprise I told you about," I said as we stepped out of the dining room.

"I know," said Jamie with a straight face. "You're going to teach me a hundred more new laws of Sabbath and then make me wonder why Christians don't observe them."

"No, not quite, Jamie. I'm going to take you someplace no tour group, Christian or Jewish, will ever take you."

"That sounds to me like a travel agent's pickup line, Rabbi," Jamie said with a laugh.

"This is for real, Jamie. I'm taking you to Meah Shearim for a *Shabbat tisch.*"

"What's that?" he asked.

"Literally it means 'table.' It's also sometimes called a *fab-rengen*. It refers to the Friday night gathering of the Hassidic community with their Rebbe, essentially a male-only bonding party of the faithful with their Rebbe."

"But won't we stand out there?" Jamie said in panic.

"Like a sore thumb," I replied.

יהוה

Most of my family remained in Israel after my grandparents emigrated to America in the 1920s. They became Karliner Hassidim. The term refers to the homeplace of the original Rebbe of this particular community of Hassidim. He came from the village of Karlin in Russia. My grandfather, who was born in what was then Palestine, was one of eight brothers and sisters. He, along with one sister and brother, moved to America during the Arab riots and a period of horrible poverty in Palestine. The rest of the family, along with my entire family on my grandmother's side, remained in Israel. While my grandfather stayed Orthodox, he shaved off his beard and earlocks on the boat to America and stopped wearing the long black coat and fur hat, characteristics of Hassidim, in order not to stand out. And while my family in Israel encountered tremendous hardships in the ensuing decades, they were, relatively speaking, the fortunate ones. For most Jews then lived in Europe, and they were wiped out in the Holocaust.

I, too, was nervous about going to the Karlin shul for the tisch. I have often wondered if my Israeli Hassidic family viewed my grandparents (and, by extension, me) as traitors for leaving Israel and abandoning them back in 1929. And given the fact that I dress and look like any other American, I often felt they viewed me as an assimilated *goy*.

יְהוָֹה

"I must admit to you, Jamie, I'm a bit nervous myself about going. While I speak Hebrew fluently, I can barely speak Yiddish, which is the language they are most conversant in, let alone feel comfortable shmoozing with them in it."

Hassidim usually reserve Hebrew, *lashon hakodesh*, the holy language, for prayer, and use Yiddish, a popularized form of German, for mundane discourse.

"I remember once walking in Jerusalem with one of my Hassidic cousins who was telling me how wrong it was to use Hebrew for regular conversations and how it should be used only for holy speech like prayer and *Torah* study. At that moment, we happened to pass a teenage couple kissing and overhear the boy declaring to his girlfriend, *'Ani ohev otach.'* I love you. 'You see what I mean?' said my cousin, as if proving his point."

"No offense, Rabbi, but your family seems pretty reactionary and extreme," said Jamie.

"Well, Jamie, they're actually very tolerant and loving toward me in spite of our religious differences. Moreover, they are strongly supportive of the State of Israel and even serve in the army. Most Hassidim do not serve in the army, and some do not even accept the legitimacy of Israel. One segment of Hassidim called the *Neturay Karta* are so fanatical they regularly condemn the State of Israel."

"Why?"

I had really stumped Jamie with this one.

"For three reasons. First, because Israel is not a theocracy guided by Jewish law. Second, the people who govern the nation are, by and large, not Orthodox. Finally, they believe we must not preempt the messiah or do his work by establishing a nation state. Instead, we are to wait passively for God to establish his kingdom on earth."

"But certainly," demanded Jamie, "they must realize that were it not for the government and army of the State of Israel, they would long ago have been murdered or expelled by the Arabs."

"I agree," I said. "Frankly, it's a travesty for them to be exempt from military service. But today, tens of thousands of army-age men evade the draft by studying in a yeshiva. This is causing a seismic schism with secular Israelis who feel that these religious Jews are gleaning the benefits of living in Israel without accepting the responsibilities and risks.

"It's all politics," I continued. "The coalition government needs the religious parties to join them so they will have a majority and be able to remain in power. The draft deferment for certain men and women is one precious price the government pays for their vote. Actually, the issue has, in recent years, been brought before the Supreme Court, which essentially ruled against the ultra Orthodox deferments."

"We have enough problems in America addressing the issue of women and gays in the army," said Jamie. "I can imagine what it would be like if there were a ruling that all Amish must be drafted against their will. We'd have chaos."

"It's not exactly the same situation here, but you get the gist of it."

יהוה

We left the hotel and began the roughly thirty-minute walk to Meah Shearim. To protect the tranquility of *Shabbat*, the citizens of this ultra Orthodox Haredi neighborhood block cars from entering their neighborhood and place steel barricades at the entrances to ensure compliance. I have come to tolerate and even respect these Jews for trying to insulate themselves from what they see as society's corruptive values by creating enclaves where they can live undisturbed by cars passing through and desecrating the *Shabbat* atmosphere.

At the same time, I have become convinced that much as we may try, it is virtually impossible today to ghettoize our children and shield them from modernity and all its concomitant negative baggage. Moreover, efforts to do so can, and often do, clash with the sensibilities of secular Israelis who do not want Heredi practices to impinge upon their lives. Instances like the controversy regarding Bar Ilan Street—a main access road passing through a Haredi neighborhood which the Haredim have for years sought to close on *Shabbat*—erupt frequently and cause discord and tension between the two factions of Israeli society.

יְהֹוָה

Jamie and I reached the Karlin Hassidic *shul*, synagogue, which looked more like a storefront than the kind of modern edifice Americans are accustomed to, and entered it with trepidation. I wondered how we—the Americanized Jewish rabbi and the non-Jewish journalist—would be accepted. As we walked in, a sea of black coats, among them, my great uncle, greeted us.

"*Shalom Aleichem! Iz mein mishpachah fun America!*" said my uncle enthusiastically to his friends. "Welcome! It's my family from America!" Ever since I was a child it was drummed into me that my family was among the most prominent in Jerusalem and that we could trace our roots back eight generations in that holy city. My family had *yichus*, good lineage and standing, because of the long line of important rabbis in the family.

"*Zetzach mit mir*," my cousin said and beckoned. "Come sit with me." Jamie and I sat down on a narrow, dilapidated wooden bench pressed up against a long, equally narrow table. The Rebbe was at the head of the table. Everyone, it seemed, was staring at us suspiciously.

"I should have worn my paisley Hawaiian shirt," said Jamie jokingly. "Then we really would have fit in."

We had arrived a bit late. The Hassidim were passing around *challah*, the *Shabbat* bread, and eating their meal. Each of them took off a piece of bread, dipped it into the salad, and ate it with their fingers, no fork or napkin in sight.

"A hygienist from the Board of Health would have a field day here," Jamie whispered to me.

"Your Board of Health hygienist would have a lot to write about at your Eucharist service, too, considering you all sip from the same cup of wine."

"Where are the women?" Jamie asked.

"They don't come Friday night to the tisch, but for prayer services. They sit up there and peek through the tiny holes in the divider," I said, pointing to the balcony that was virtually hidden by wooden boards reaching the ceiling.

Most Orthodox congregations today still have separate pews for men and women so that men won't be distracted by sexual thoughts during prayer services. Some of the older, European-type synagogues, and all Hassidic synagogues today, still have a balcony for the women.

Hundreds of Hassidim were gathered in the shul, all trying to get a glimpse of the Rebbe and, if lucky, have their eyes meet.

They were humming a song, swaying back and forth trancelike, deep in contemplation.

"What are they doing?" Jamie asked.

"They are striving for *dveikut*, which means attachment or union with God. Hassidim, in contrast with mainline Orthodoxy, focus more on song and prayer than on intellect and Talmudic study." The room was tiny and jampacked. Everyone was sitting uncomfortably up against one another. And yet the heightened spirituality that radiated through the room was profound. The oneness those men felt with God and with one another was powerful and discernible. It wasn't so much a somber atmosphere as it was an intense, serious one.

My cousin turned to me and said in Yiddish, "Do you want to greet the Rebbe?"

"Um, I don't know," I said, stuttering nervously in broken Yiddish. "How do you think he will react to me?"

"Let's find out," said my cousin with a confident smile on his face.

יהוה

Hassidim are proud of their Rebbe. Actually, they stand in awe of him. They believe that he has intercessory powers with God and is able to perform miracles on their behalf. I debated whether or not to tell my cousin that Jamie was not Jewish, and a journalist to boot—two strikes against him since Hassidim tend to be suspicious of both. Jamie was wearing the black velvet yarmulke I had given him earlier. He looked like he could be any secular American Jew. I debated whether to tell the Rebbe that Jamie was a Baptist Christian (though Jamie was still unsure about that) or to stretch the truth by saying he was an unobservant American acquaintance searching for spiritual meaning in his life (which he was). There are many *baalei tshuvah* or "born again" Jews today all around the world, young people who were brought up in a secular Jewish home who are now rediscovering their Jewish identity and coming back to *Yiddishkeit*—the word ultra Orthodox Jews use for Judaism. Most become Orthodox, often to the dismay of their parents who sometimes even prefer that they had become Buddhists instead. Then, at least, the children would not demand that the parents make their home kosher for them to eat in.

I was torn by the moral dilemma before me. Should I stretch the truth with the Rebbe in order to show my friend this Hassidic community from which I came and of which I was so proud, a community so terribly misunderstood by the outside world—by Jewish and non-Jewish alike? Or should I risk the potential embarrassment of telling the Rebbe honestly that this man with me was a Christian journalist seeking to better understand Jewish life from the inside?

Before I could resolve the matter, my cousin took me by the hand and walked us into the throngs. It was like the Red Sea parting, with people moving aside for us as we passed through and came to within inches of the Rebbe.

Jamie and I lifted our glass of wine as we had seen others do and together we said, *"Gut Shabbes."* The Rebbe looked deeply into my eyes. I felt his gaze penetrating me, as if he could really understand me, sinner that I was. I felt embarrassed, guilty, and nervous all at the same time. Meanwhile, the Hassidim continued their singing, seemingly oblivious to the curiosity before them. The Rebbe gestured with his hand toward my cousin. *"Mishpachah fun America?"* he asked. "Family from America?"

Before my cousin could respond I said, *"Yah, mein nomin iz* Yechiel Zvi Eckstein."

The Rebbe gazed into my eyes again. *"Kum, zetzach mit mire."* He broke out in a big warm smile. "Come sit here next to me." And then, in perfect English, he added, "I knew your grandparents well."

I felt Jamie's sweaty palm squeezing my hand, trying to pull me away, but it was too late. We sat down to the Rebbe's right on the seats that had suddenly become vacated for us, the Rebbe's "special guests" from America. The Hassidim squeezed over and were sitting almost on each other's lap. It reminded me of the paintings I had seen of Jesus with his disciples at the Last Supper. Of course, I wasn't about to share that image with the Rebbe.

"Gut Shabbes," said the Rebbe to Jamie who, with all his wits about him, responded in perfect Yiddish, *"Gut Shabbes."* The Rebbe asked if he was also *mishpachah.*

"No, he's a friend," I quickly interjected, praying the Rebbe would not pursue the matter. Fortunately, my moral integrity was not put to the test. The Rebbe was silent.

I joined in the singing. After a few moments, even Jamie started to get into it.

"Don't push it," I said. "Pretend you're tone deaf and too embarrassed to sing."

Suddenly, out of nowhere, the Rebbe turned to Jamie and asked, *"Du bist a journalist?"*

I was shocked and ready to crawl under the table. But Jamie, cool as a cucumber, nodded his head affirmatively. The Rebbe looked at him for a second, chuckled, and then said, in English, "That's okay, you can sit here too."

Jamie, turning ashen, whispered to me, "How the hell did he figure out I was a journalist?"

I looked at him, smiled, and said matter of factly, "That's why he's the Rebbe."

We sat there swaying with the crowd for roughly a half-hour. I kept wondering what was going on in Jamie's head. I, at least, shared a common faith, heritage, and peoplehood with these Hassidim. They were, in a very real sense, my family. I had a frame of reference for them and understood everything they were saying. I even knew some of the melodies they were singing. But what was Jamie thinking? The experience must have been totally foreign and "other" to him. I wondered whether he was viewing this Hassidic *tisch* the same way I might feel were I to visit an Amish gathering. I realized again that only when one hears the music from the inside can its dulcet sounds, ineffable grandeur, and overwhelming beauty be truly appreciated.

Suddenly, as if anticipating my question or perhaps needing to express himself, Jamie suddenly said, "I feel like I've just been transported back in time to a small eighteenth-century *shtetle* [village] in Poland. You know the kind, like the one I saw in *Fiddler on the Roof*, with wooden floors so dusty that when a person walks on them he can see a cloud of dust rising all around him. Kids running around, men with beards, black hats, and coats—the whole shtick," he said, showing off his familiarity with the New York slang.

"And even though I can't understand one word of what they're saying or singing, and it's nothing like the hymns I remember from my childhood in church, in a strange way I can feel God's presence here in this crowded room. I feel spiritually uplifted and closer to God than I have in a long time, especially when I realize we are worshiping the same divine father, each in our own way.

"But you know what surprises me most? Instead of feeling insecure and threatened as a Christian by this experience, I am energized by it. I actually feel stronger in my Christian faith, renewed and restored as a Christian, by having come here, strange as that may sound. What do you think, Rabbi?" he asked.

"I think that God is already answering your prayer at the Wall, Jamie."

After a few moments of silence, I said, "Look over there," pointing to the front of the synagogue. "On top of the Ark. Do you see the Ten Commandments? They are yours, too. Do you remember that Paul in the book of Romans, chapter nine, said that by God's grace and love you gentiles were grafted onto the rich olive tree of Israel and are now of the seed of Abraham? That is a profound lesson of the shared tradition of Christians and Jews. Of course, you gentiles should also remember his warning to you not to become haughty with your new heritage, for the root supports the branch and not the branch the root. It's almost as if Paul realized that just a few centuries later Marcian and his followers would try to sever the link between Christianity and its Jewish roots.

"Jamie, I believe deeply that, different as we are, you and I are spiritually united in so many ways. We share our morality and belief in the brotherhood of man under God, our devotion to the God of Israel and, hopefully, with this trip, a love for the land and people of Israel."

"'How good and how pleasant it is,' Jamie added, quoting from the Psalms, 'for brethren to dwell together in unity.' And, how ironic that it took a totally alien experience—going to a Hassidic *tisch* on *Shabbat* in Jerusalem—for me to be strengthened as a Christian."

"No," I interjected, "for us *both* to be strengthened in our respective faiths, and for us both to realize how united we truly are."

יְהוָה

As we left the little *shul*, I wondered again what my life would have been like had my grandparents not left their Hassidic cloister in Israel—less sophisticated and worldly, to be sure, and probably a lot poorer, too. But possibly much richer and more spiritually fulfilled. In America, in the best of Jewish communities, even on the Sabbath and in the most meaningful of synagogue services, I still feel a sense of existential alienation, estrangement, and rootlessness that I do not feel anywhere in Israel, any day of the week.

Here, in just one hour, I felt part of something greater, more spiritually satisfying, more wondrous and fulfilling and refreshing than anything I had ever experienced in the U.S. That is why I feel so comfortable, at home and alive in Israel. Here, for me, God is so real, self-evident, and close. Here, I can feel his presence so readily and powerfully. Perhaps this is my reward for striving to feel his eclipsed presence in the diaspora when I am there.

I love America deeply and am grateful for the privilege of having grown up and lived there. But when I go to Jerusalem, I feel I've returned home. I also love modernity and can't even think of what life would be like without my daily fix of the *New York Times* and Starbucks coffee. But what had I given up in the process? What price was I paying for that privilege of living in America and embracing modernity?

יהוה

Walking back to our hotel through the narrow, cobble-stone alleyways of Meah Shearim late at night, Jamie and I could hear the voices of children singing *Shabbat* songs from the verandas above us. Their singing reminded me of the words of the prophet who promised hope and joy in the place of despair for the people of Israel. "There will yet be heard in the cities of Judah and outskirts of Jerusalem, the voice of joy and the voice of gladness." Children and families were singing *zemiros* together, songs of praise to God for the *Shabbat*. There's nothing in the world that compares with that experience of a true *Shabbat* in Jerusalem. From within, it is heaven on earth, a foretaste of the world to come.

"I owe you an apology," said Jamie softly. "I'm sorry I belittled the *Shabbat* earlier by calling it restrictive and burdensome."

"That's okay, Jamie. I understand that from the outside it may appear that way. I'm glad you got to see it from within and feel its beauty. I believe deeply that the people of Israel will prevail, with God's help, and meet every future adversity. "But, Jamie, it is the sanctity and sweetness of those singing kids and their love-filled devotional homes, committed as they are to the minutiae of Jewish law, that will keep us Jews and our faith alive. *Am Yisrael chai*, the people of Israel lives." I declared.

"*Veyichyeh*, and shall live," added Jamie, to my absolute surprise and joy.

יהוה

Saturday morning I let Jamie sleep in while I attended *Shabbat* morning services at a synagogue near the hotel. In the afternoon, while Jamie went off on his own, I ate lunch, studied *Torah,* and then took a short nap. As nightfall approached, Jamie rejoined me at the synagogue nearby where I recited *maariv* and the *havdalah*, separation ceremony, over a glass of wine, a two-wicked candle, and sweet smelling spices. The Sabbath had passed, and our spirit needed to be revived. "Have no fear, my servant, Jacob, for God is with you," I sang, confident in God's providence and protection as we faced the new week.

In the Jewish tradition, the Sabbath is not so much a day of rest enabling us to function better the remainder of the week. Rather, it is the culmination of all the other days, the acme experience to which the rest of the week points and looks forward.

יהוה

"It's Saturday night, let's hit the town!" Jamie said.

"Okay," I said. "Nothing wrong with some good clean fun."

We walked back to the Ben Yehudah Street pedestrian mall, named after Yitzhak ben Yehudah, who, at the turn of the twentieth century, led the revival of the ancient Hebrew language. As quiet and deserted as it was here on *Shabbat*, it seemed like everyone in Jerusalem was "hanging out" here on Saturday night. Stores were open, buses were running, the pulse of the city was throbbing and alive. Guys with ponytails and girls straight out of the 1960s with braided bracelets and cheap handmade earrings, a music group from Guatemala, a Russian violinist, and a French mime crowded the street, trying to collect a few shekels from passersby. We enjoyed walking around, looking at the people, and eating a falafel as we went.

We walked back to the hotel and watched TV for a few minutes before going to sleep. Since cable was only just beginning to make inroads in the Israeli market—primarily because of the inordinate government control and regulation over the airwaves—the two main channels stopped airing programs at midnight.

It didn't take much to get me emotional in Jerusalem. Even small things like the close of television programs at midnight moved me deeply. Before going off the air, the national anthem, "Hatikvah," was played, with the Israeli blue-and-white flag fluttering in the wind on the screen. This was followed by the *psuko shel yom,* verse of the day, a reading from Scriptures. My eyes got teary. I was filled with pride to be part of a people that was resurrected from centuries of exile and oppression, to be part of a nation that fought against the odds and overcame those who sought to obliterate them from the world. And this ancient yet modern nation, closed the day, every day, with the soul-piercing strains of "Hatikvah," the hope, and with words from the *Torah*. There is an old Yiddish adage, "Shver tzu zein a yid." It is hard to be a Jew. While true, moments like that, at the close of each and every normal day, I felt like adding, "Ober iz gut tzu zein a yid." It's good to be a Jew.

Thank you, God, for making me part of this beautiful, holy people, Israel.

CHAPTER NINE

SUNDAY MORNING WALK

"**P**hooey! It's terrible," said Jamie with a grimace to the waitress as he sent back his breakfast coffee. She brought him a new cup, which was not much better.

"I find myself dreaming about a good cup of Starbucks. Forget the latte and cappuccino. I'll settle for plain coffee of the day."

"Me, too," I chimed in. "But you should know that just five years ago, the coffee in Israel was even worse. And decent toilet paper was something you had to bring with you from America."

I found myself more patient with irritants like bad coffee and burdensome bureaucracy and more understanding of Israel's inadequacies than I had been in earlier years.

While Israel is not exactly a Third World country or banana republic—quite the contrary, she's incredibly advanced—she is still a young nation that has faced wars and existential threats from her inception to this very day. It's incredible how far Israel has come in such a short time and in the face of such tremendous adversity. In the not-too-distant future, Israel will reach, and even surpass,

America's and Japan's records in technological achievements. But for the time being, America's standards of excellence, particularly in product quality and service, are the ideals to which this nascent country still aspires.

"Why do you give me a whole spiel when all I said was that the coffee is lousy?" Jamie asked, complaining.

"I'm just trying to make the point that it's all a question of attitude. The Bible tells us to 'look for the good in Jerusalem' and, indeed, for the good in all people and situations. Sure, it's easy to find fault with many aspects of Israeli life. But it's just as easy to look for the good qualities. The same is true regarding the Israeli people who, I admit, have rough edges and may appear cold and callous. But scratch the surface and you'll find there's a lot of good there, too. Did you know that's why people born in Israel are called *sabras,* after the cactus plant whose fruit is prickly on the outside but sweet on the inside?"

יהוה,

There is much in Israeli society to criticize, particularly the fact that so much of life is infused with politics. Is Israel forthcoming enough with the Palestinians? Is she too forthcoming? How much land should she give away for the possibility of peace? Will a peace treaty hold? Will an agreement lead to another war? Will Israel's security be compromised because she gave away the very land that would have protected her? Is a real and lasting peace possible in the Middle East? These tough questions are splitting the country down the middle.

That very day I opened the newspaper to read that a group of Israeli settlers in the Golan Heights, fearing that Israel would give away their homes, celebrated a mock wedding between them and the land. They vowed never to leave the Golan. Across the street hecklers were calling for an annulment of the marriage. Just another day in the life of Israel.

יְהוָה

We hopped on a city bus, the best way to tour the city and get a feel for its pulse and people. Sitting opposite us was a beautiful Ethiopian girl with jet-black hair dressed in a crisp, Israeli army uniform. "Wow," I heard Jamie mutter under his breath. He echoed my thoughts exactly. As the Bible says, "I am black and beautiful."

Sensing that Jamie was about to try a pickup line on her, I warned him, "Better not mess with her, Jamie. See what she's holding on her shoulder? An Uzi submachine gun. And she knows how to use it, too!"

Of course, that didn't stop Jamie one bit. But then again, he didn't get very far with the line, "Can you show me how to shoot your gun?"

יְהוָה

Beep. Beep. Beep. This is Israel News from Jerusalem. The driver raised the volume on the radio so people on the bus could hear. Immediately, everyone was quiet. The newscaster somberly announced that the head of the urology department at one of Israel's major hospitals was killed in a traffic accident earlier that day on the Jerusalem–Tel Aviv highway. What a waste! And what a horrible situation.

Accidents in Israel are caused not so much by drunk drivers as by overly aggressive sober ones. Even bus drivers. Especially bus drivers.

Everything is fast paced. The buses begin moving before people sit down. Drivers even collect fares and give change while driving. But buses are a great laboratory for studying the diversity of the Israeli people. One can see all sorts of people, black and white, Sephardic and Ashkenazic, religious and secular, Arab and Jew, young and old, men and women, modern Orthodox and Haredi, Israeli born and foreign workers—even Thai, Vietnamese, and Romanian. The differences among them are stark, from their facial features to the way they dress, from the language they speak to the kind of bags they carry. Israel is truly the melting pot of the world. New York is a distant second place.

יהוה

"Did you know that a bus driver in Israel makes more than a doctor?" I asked Jamie. "And he is even more highly regarded than rabbis! There's a joke about that. A rabbi and bus driver died and went to the heavenly gates. God immediately let the bus driver enter but made the rabbi wait a few months. When finally allowed in, the rabbi was seated in a lower section of heaven than the bus driver. Naturally, the rabbi demanded an explanation from God for his poor treatment. So God responded, 'When you preached and taught *Torah*, people slept; but when the bus driver drove, people prayed.'"

"Ha-ha," laughed Jamie, more out of courtesy than actual amusement.

יהוה

It is not uncommon to hear military planes streaking overhead and breaking the sound barrier in Jerusalem. Israelis are proud of their fighter pilots, as well they should be. They're among the best in the world. Whether sitting quietly on a bus or eating a falafel in a pedestrian mall, one is reminded once again that this is a war zone. No matter where one is in Israel, the border is just a few kilometers away. A sobering thought, indeed.

יהוה,

No matter how comfortable I feel in Israel and how often I visit, there is no getting used to seeing seventeen-year-old girls carrying submachine guns slung over their shoulders, walking around as if it was the most natural thing in the world. Though women do not serve in fighting units, they play an integral role in the military, not just as doctors, nurses, secretaries, and drivers, but also as teachers and trainers in all areas of warfare, including marksmanship and counterterrorism. I have a daughter who's seventeen—she's my little baby. Call me chauvinistic, okay. Misogynist, okay. But I hope I never get used to seeing these kids with guns.

The border can be clearly seen—the green fields end and the brown begin. Each time I visit Israel, I see more green, more construction, more people inhabiting and cultivating the land. Israel strives to make every inch of land productive, to redeem it from its centuries of neglect and barrenness. I explained to Jamie the mystical Jewish principle that the land of Israel will refuse to bear fruit when its natural partner, Israel, does not dwell on it.

When Mark Twain visited Israel in the late 1800s, he described the land of Israel as desolate, uncultivated, swampy, and malaria-infested. That was before the people of Israel returned to the land. Today, the land's marriage to the Jewish people has led to its being richly blessed. Today, it bears much sweet fruit.

"Where are we headed today?" Jamie asked softly.

"Today we go to *Yad Vashem*, the Holocaust memorial site."

"I told you, Rabbi," he demurred, "my job here is to learn the ethos of the people, not to see the memorial sites.

"I understand," I said. "That is precisely why we began our visit by first praying at the Wall. The next place to go is *Yad Vashem*. You will never understand the psyche of the Jewish people or the miracle of Israel's birth without walking through those life-transforming doors. The road to Jerusalem is paved over the ashes of Auschwitz, Buchenwald, Treblinka, and all the other death camps. We must walk that road today, Jamie, as painful as it is."

"Okay! You're the boss," Jamie said in resignation. "First, let's go for a walk. I need to work off that huge breakfast!"

Sunday is a regular workday in Israel. The streets are busy with children going back to school, soldiers returning to their bases, and people rushing back to work. We passed a group of teenage boys with ponytails and earrings, waiting in line to get on a bus.

"Ah," says Jamie, "the new Israeli. Just as King David, no doubt, envisaged him when he established this city."

"I must admit that sometimes I am embarrassed by my own people. Unfortunately, many of us are not as spiritually inclined as we should be. We've been afflicted by secularism, materialism, and other destructive values not part of the original Zionist dream.

"Israeli youth today are different from their parents and grandparents, and so are their values. Most would probably rather go to a mall, watch MTV, and play their stereo than build a new nation and fulfill the Zionist ideal. I must admit, Jamie, I once even felt that the young generation of Palestinians, desperately seeking a homeland and motivated by a sense of purpose, had a stronger sense of idealism than many of today's Israeli youth who have become soft on freedom and complacent about their liberties."

יְהֹוָה

The minute those words left my mouth, I felt guilty. Was I speaking badly of my own brothers and sisters? This community of survivors shunned by the world and rejected as pariahs? This "people that dwelleth alone"? Was I maligning the youths of this Jewish nation that, just a few decades ago, were thrown into the ovens and crematoriums of Nazi Europe? How could I possibly do that in good conscience?

Those young Israeli men would soon be spending three years of their lives serving in the army, defending the land and people of Israel. Some of them would likely be maimed and even killed. Who gave me the right, living as I do in the comfort and safety of Chicago, to judge these kids and, even worse, spread such aspersions, especially to someone not part of my Jewish family? And all because of the way the kids looked? The heads of the ten tribes of Israel were punished for doubting God's ability to deliver his people and conquer the land. And there I was maligning my fellow Jews and casting unfair judgments on their character, on the very people God has chosen to defend his nation of Israel, because they had ponytails and earrings! Indeed, as the Bible says, "man sees only what is visible, the LORD sees into the heart."

If God chooses to carry out his will through "secular, materialistic Jews," who am I to question him? Or to judge his partners in that redemption? Have I insufficient trust in God's ability to fulfill his promise in *his* way, not mine? Did I not realize that these young people, too, are the holy instruments of God's will in the world? They may be more or less observant of Jewish law, but they are religious Jews, whether they know it or not.

I was, at that moment, filled with a profound love for my people, *all* my people. I prayed for forgiveness for judging them so harshly, for seeing only the ephemeral and negative, and for not recognizing that these, too, are God's holy partners in the building and fixing of the world.

I was reminded of the story of a rabbi who once saw one of his congregants violating Jewish law by smoking a cigarette on the Sabbath.

"My son," said the rabbi gently, "perhaps you do not know that today is the Sabbath?"

"Yes, I know," the man responded wryly to the rabbi.

"Then surely you do not realize that smoking is prohibited on the Sabbath," said the rabbi, giving him the benefit of the doubt.

"I am fully aware of my transgression," responded the congregant. "Nevertheless, I choose to smoke today."

Finally, the rabbi lifted up his hands to heaven and cried out, "Lord, your people may not be Sabbath observers, but look at how wonderful they are. They always tell the truth." The point being, of course, that there's always something good to find in others.

In the early 1960s, Soviet Jews were sometimes maligned by their Jewish brethren as being more secular and communist than truly Jewish. Yet God was able to imbue them with His spirit despite decades of communist repression, and to instill in them a yearning to live in freedom as Jews and to leave mother Russia for their ancient homeland, Israel. Who would have thought these people, so distant from their Jewish faith and heritage, could again become a holy people? But we are the children of Abraham and Sarah, with promises to keep and a destiny to fulfill.

I was haunted by the criticisms I had leveled at today's Israeli youth and couldn't get them out of my mind. At that moment I made a solemn pledge never again to judge others and never again to speak in a derogatory manner of these secular, materialistic people, my people, these children who put their lives on the line defending the nation and me. As the gentile prophet Balaam recognized after seeking to curse Israel, these are a holy people, a blessed people. I pledged to continue teaching Jews and gentiles of God's sovereignty, to help them strive for holiness, and to assist them in bringing God's presence into their lives. I would try to sensitize those who did not see the miraculous in the birth of Israel and the hand of God in her survival. I would try to help them become more spiritually attuned. But I would never judge them again. I would live my life with greater love toward these, my people, who risk their lives defending my nation, Israel. I vowed never again to judge my people, earrings and all! Never again.

יהוה

By then, we had walked to the intersection of King George and Jaffa Streets, the hub of Jerusalem's downtown, right off the Ben Yehuda pedestrian mall. We were looking for a great pizza restaurant that had just opened somewhere in the area. Despite the terrorist bombings, native Israelis and tourists alike hang out there.

A Christian missionary walked by, cheerfully singing out loud. He stopped in front of a group of bearded, longhaired German hikers sitting on the ground with knapsacks at their side.

"You look like Yeshua," the missionary said to one of them.

"And you must be John the Baptist," the young German responded in broken English.

A woman's voice suddenly rang out. "Oh my God! Yechiel, is that you?!"

It was Esther. I had studied as a teenager at a yeshiva in Israel with her husband and had come to know her later on. They were from South Africa and, after a few years of marriage, had decided to make *aliyah* to Israel. We hugged.

"How are your three kids, Esther?" I asked, remembering a detail I usually forget.

"*Baruch Hashem*," she said, all excited. "Thank God."

"And how's Shmulik?" I asked.

Suddenly her face dropped. "I guess you haven't heard."

"Heard what?" I asked.

"Shmulik was killed on the Lebanese border a few months ago, Yechiel."

I was struck speechless. Shmulik was my *chavrutah* or study partner at yeshiva. He was brilliant, with a far greater acumen and quicker grasp of Talmud than I ever possessed. We both dreamed of living in Israel one day—as permanent residents, not as visiting students. Shmulik fulfilled his dream. And now I learned that Shmulik also paid the ultimate price, sacrificing his life for the Jewish people.

I was overcome with tremendous sadness, guilt, and feelings of unworthiness. What had I done to earn the privilege of walking in this land so freely, visiting the holy sites, and leisurely strolling around Jaffa Street looking for good pizza? Nothing. Shmulik, on the other hand, had paid for that right. He earned that privilege, for himself and his family. So did all the other Israelis who served in the military and fought in the wars. Even Israeli civilians, who spent frightening days and nights sitting in sealed rooms while Iraq lobbed suspected biological and chemical missiles at them, had a right to enjoy this land. But me?

I felt like a foreigner in my own home, distanced from Israeli Jews, a freeloader who had not paid his dues. I felt a barrier between this land and me, a chasm between my fulfillment as a Jew and me, between the Israeli people and me. Shmulik had earned his place. I, in sharp contrast, was an unencumbered tourist passing through, reaping the spoils of Shmulik's sacrifice. I was haunted by Moses' admonition to the two and a half tribes who sought to remain on the east bank of the Jordan River instead of joining the other tribes to fight the Canaanites. I felt as if God was saying to me, "Your brothers will go to war and you will sit in Chicago?" I realized how utterly scandalous it was for me to live in far-off Chicago and visit Israel a few times a year, but not cast my destiny with my brothers and sisters here, whatever that destiny might be, even if it might be Shmulik's.

יְהֹוָה

The mood of the country is different each time I go to Israel. I remember both the glee after the victorious 1967 Six Day War and the gloom after the 1973 War and the many terrorist attacks Israel has endured since. There were times that it seemed all hope had been sapped from the people. And other times that it seemed, paradoxically, that adverse events strengthened Israel's will and resolve.

The impact of the tourism industry on life in Israel is extensive and profound. Not only does it provide the economy with a major infusion of foreign capital, but also significant numbers of people are dependent on it, service workers, manufacturers, busboys, chambermaids, tour guides, cab drivers, hoteliers, restaurateurs. Just as important, tourists give Israelis the encouraging feeling that they are not alone in their struggle for survival, a pride that their nation is worth visiting, and a strong assurance that foreigners feel secure enough to be with the Israeli people to visit the land.

"This month, you see tour buses all over the country," one tour guide, delighted with the influx of visitors, had said to me earlier that day. "Last month, the place was deserted. God forbid, were we to have another bombing here, tourism will dry up all over again."

יהוה

We noticed a little girl, maybe six years old, walking to a public bus stop on her way to school and carrying a back-pack almost as big as she was.

"I would never let my little kids walk alone like that or take public transportation to school, and I live in a Chicago suburb," I commented to Jamie.

יהוה

Kids seem to mature much earlier in Israel, perhaps because they are given greater responsibility at a younger age than in the United States. By the time they go to the army when they are eighteen, they have been exposed, almost on a daily basis, to the mortal struggle most of us in America are, thank God, spared. The silver lining is that it builds character and maturity and fosters respect for parents and elders. It also teaches young people to take life more seriously and less for granted than the way we do in the U.S.

While Israelis are not known for their etiquette and proper manners, they exhibit great respect for the elderly. It is not unusual to see people jump up from their seats on the bus to compete for the privilege of giving them up for the elderly. Indeed, young people will be publicly chastised for failing to do so. Israeli society also tries to find meaningful roles for the elderly to play—enlisting their help to care for children in day-care programs, to check people's bags for bombs at public buildings, and so forth. Whether this deferential attitude stems from a strong sense of community, whether it is a vestige of the society's socialist background where everyone has a function and must pull his or her own weight, or whether it is simply a product of time-honored ethical Jewish values, I do not know. But in Israel the elderly are made to feel like they are worthy of value and that they have something yet to contribute to the building of the nation.

יהוה

We were walking on the Ben Yehuda mall, looking at the store windows and gazing at the array of young people hanging out there.

"Why do men wear different color yarmulkes on their heads? Jamie asked. "And why are some knitted, others leather, and still others velvet, like the one you gave me to wear?"

His query gave me the opportunity to explain some of the differences among Orthodox Jews.

"First, there are the modern Orthodox like myself who usually wear knitted, colored, or patterned yarmulkes and who are generally more tolerant of modernity. This group values secular studies and a college education, affirms equal rights for women, and generally has more positive views of non-Jews. They strongly support the State of Israel, serve in the army, and most feel linked to historical Zionist ideals. They often are also the settlers who are reluctant to give up land for peace in the belief that God gave it as an eternal inheritance to Israel, whose duty it is to settle it.

"A second group of Orthodox is the more fundamentalist yeshiva type, who tend to be more dogmatic in their theology, disdainful of modernity and its secular values, and are less inclined than the modern Orthodox to synthesize tradition with modernity. You can identify them by their trimmed beards and their attire of black suits, black hats, and white shirts.

"The third group are the *Hassidim* who, like the black-hatters, have beards and wear black suits, but who also wear fedoras and long jackets and on *Shabbat* fur hats called *shtreimals*. They are generally the most separatist of all, living in separate enclaves and eschewing the negative trappings of modernity. They oppose secular studies and rarely serve in the Israeli army.

"But these are just thumbnail sketches of the Orthodox community. There's much more that distinguishes each of these three strains of Orthodox Jews, and there're many more shades of differences within each category. Let me put it in categories you may better relate to. The three types of Orthodox Jews loosely correspond to the three groups of evangelical Christians. The modern Orthodox are most akin to mainline evangelicals as represented by leaders like Billy Graham. Black-hatters are most similar to Baptist fundamentalists and people like Jerry Falwell. And the Hassidim are most like charismatics and Pentecostals and leaders such as Pat Robertson."

יְהוָה

I had arranged to meet an old friend, Dov, a top attorney in the United States, who had moved to Israel ten years ago. The three of us sat down at one of the outdoor cafés and chatted over cappuccino. Dov told me he works twice as hard in Israel for a quarter of the salary he had in the States. He said he struggles to get by on his income and pays fifty percent to taxes, but he has no regrets.

"Do you ever think about moving back to the States, Dov?" I asked.

"Never," he replied emphatically. "Here, I can make a real contribution to the building of our Jewish nation and I can play a real role in the unfolding drama of our people. Here I am truly alive as a Jew. More important, my kids are growing up as proud and fulfilled Jews. It's true we don't have a big family house and pool like we had in the States. But the trade-offs are definitely worth it. I am convinced I made the right decision, and I have absolutely no misgivings. I am convinced that those Jews remaining in the States just don't realize what they're missing, what they're giving up, the heavy price in personal satisfaction and fulfillment they're paying for their lifestyle *al seer habasar* [the Hebrew term used in the Bible to describe the Egyptian 'flesh pots']. And that doesn't even begin to take into account the great likelihood that their children will marry out of the faith."

Dov's words cut through me like a dagger. Had I, indeed, compromised my Jewish idealism by seeking the good life? Had I become so inured and complacent with my lifestyle in America and so comfortable as to be deaf to God's calling me, and all American Jews, to return home to Israel? I love America and regard it as my country. But, I wondered, had I forgotten that ultimately America for the Jew is still the diaspora not exile? Had I lost sight of my own deep belief that the only place for a Jew to live a complete and fulfilled life is in Israel?

יהוה

Leaving the café, Jamie and I by chance strolled right by a place that was familiar to me, the yeshiva where I had studied as a teenager. We entered the building and were immediately accosted by a cacophony of sounds—teenage boys studying with *hitlahavut,* exuberance.

"A far cry from the New York public library," shouted Jamie, bewildered by the intensity, body language, and hand gestures of the roughly two hundred and fifty students in the study hall. "What are they doing? They look like they're arguing, almost fighting."

"They're studying Talmud, Jamie," I responded with equanimity. "The oral law explaining the Bible. They're trying to understand the text and grasp its truths. They're seeking out God's will for man in those texts. That's why they're so animated."

"Is that how Jesus studied the scriptures in his time?" Jamie asked.

"Probably," I said. "There were *Torah* academies just like this one in Israel during his time, too."

יְהוָה

We left the yeshiva and began walking back to the hotel. Politics was evident throughout Israel, tucked in among the small kiosks selling fresh carrot juice—a popular drink here—and in storefronts selling everything from mattresses to religious trinkets. Everywhere we went we found people pushing their religious or political points of view. Walking down the street, we came across a group of teenagers carrying placards favoring the prime minister. Immediately behind them were others bitterly opposed to him. Behind them were Jewish evangelists trying to persuade Jews to become *frum,* religious, and next to them some older men were collecting money for orphans and yeshivas. We saw signs on buildings, roadways, cars, and store walls with catchy mottoes like THE LAND OF ISRAEL FOR THE PEOPLE OF ISRAEL, a clarion message designed to sway the public and government not to give up land to the Arabs. To go out for a leisurely bite to eat is to subject oneself to Israel's thriving

democracy. Every Israeli has a soap box, and he doesn't hesitate to use it. Thank God for that.

יהוה,

The country is deeply divided on how to bring a true
and lasting peace to the Middle East. Many remain skeptical of Arab intentions and promises, believing they will
never be satisfied until they regain all of Israel, including
Jerusalem, and throw the Jews into the sea. The peace
process, in their eyes, is a clever Arab way of achieving
through peaceful means what they have been unable to
accomplish in battle. Others see no alternative to negoti-
ating and sacrificing land for peace, provided the Jewish
state's security is ensured. The issue is far more nuanced
and complex than this, of course. But for both sides, the
peace issue and, by extension, politics, deal with intense
life-and-death matters.

The city of Jerusalem is invigorating and pulsating.
People go about their business, talking animatedly in public places, feeling at ease and not the least bit inhibited. The
people feel at home. The pace of life is fast and high-strung,
reminding me a lot of New York's garment district. But people don't jay walk or cross the street on a red light. They
wait patiently and compliantly for the green pedestrian
light. I've always wondered why they are so acquiescent to
this rule when it goes against the grain of being an Israeli
and defying authority.

יהוה,

As we walked on the Ben Yehudah mall, we heard the
song "Jerusalem of Gold," which became popular when
Jerusalem was reunited in the 1967 War. The music was

coming from a restaurant trying to entice nostalgic American Jewish tourists to go inside.

The influence of America was evident everywhere, from the clothing displayed in store windows to the advertisements adorning the walls. And while few are complaining, many are concerned about the "McDonaldization" of Israel and the erosion of idealism that it and other American icons like Madonna, the Material Girl, have brought. Israel is certainly not a theocracy like Iran that reacts with hostility toward such influences. Nevertheless, Israel has a growing concern about American values and their corrosive effects invading the nation.

Walking around the crowded streets, both Jamie and I remarked how easy it would be for a terrorist to cause horrific carnage. But people were not allowing such thoughts to consume them. They laughed and talked, ate and argued, hugged and kissed, as people of any other nation might. Yet in contrast with other nations, there was a special pathos, more like an old country town than a bustling metropolis where people are alienated and disengaged from one another. That same intense energy can be channeled in negative directions, too. Across the street, we saw a fistfight break out in a line of people waiting to get into a crowded bus. Those people might be God's chosen, but they're not all saints!

CHAPTER TEN

OUR VISIT TO YAD VASHEM

Though I walk through a valley of deepest darkness...

We arrived at *Yad Vashem*, Israel's Holocaust memorial museum, and approached it with the same sense of awe, trepidation, and reverence that we approached the Wall just a day earlier. It is impossible to understand the psyche of the Israeli people and what impels their political sensibilities without visiting the museum. Because of its importance, every Israeli high school student, military recruit, and visiting foreign dignitary is brought to the site.

יהוה

It has not always been like this. For years, the new Israeli-born generation felt distant from the Holocaust experience, having been raised in a free, independent, and mighty state. They especially could not understand why the Jews faced their death so passively; they could not relate to their not fighting back. This feeling of invincibility and self-reliance was particularly pronounced after the Israeli victory in the

1967 Six Day War. But events like the 1973 War, which Israel almost lost, and the protracted intifadas, which have taken a devastating toll on Israeli morale, made them more keenly aware of their own vulnerabilities and more understanding of the Jews' defenseless situation in the Holocaust.

Jews interpret the meaning and implications of the Holocaust in different ways. Many ultra Orthodox victims and survivors saw it as a vicarious atonement for the sins of American Jews. Many atheistic Jews view it as positive proof that God does not exist. Israeli sabras often see it as confirmation of the classic Zionist prognosis for all diaspora existence—persecution and eradication. For their part, American Jews cite the Holocaust as proof of the need for continued vigilance in the fight against prejudice and anti-Semitism.

The Holocaust is invoked across the ideological spectrum to corroborate one's a priori worldview and, often, to promote one's own selfish, trivial, and narrow purposes. Years ago, I heard a woman lecture on the role of women in the workplace and the importance of equal pay for equal work. She closed her speech with the unconscionable remark, "After all, haven't we learned *anything* from the Holocaust?"

יהוה

I noticed two elderly men speaking Russian and proudly wearing their Soviet war medals on their jackets. I've met dozens of Russian Jews like them over the years. Many feel out of place in Israel, deprived of respect, and lacking in feelings of self-worth and belonging. They feel like a burden because they are not making a positive contribution to society. They look back nostalgically to their earlier lives in the former Soviet Union where they were treated as war heroes. The medals that they continue to wear wherever they go in

Israel are often the last vestiges of pride and dignity they possess. To paraphrase the pithy adage of Jews and the exodus, You can take the Jews out of Russia, but it's a lot harder to take Russia out of the Jews.

It is an IDF requirement that every soldier visit this site during his or her basic training. Here the future defenders of Israel become linked with their past, bonded with their fighting unit, and united with their peoplehood. Never forget the past—that is the message emanating from this site. And never allow the Jewish people to be powerless again.

Why do we Jews keep coming back? And why do we insist that others come too? Have we become overly obsessed with the Holocaust? With all the books, movies, lectures, and sermons on the subject, haven't we had enough of it already? Isn't it time for us Jews to move on? These are fair questions. But for us, the answer is simple. We are never to forget our history of sorrow. "Remember the days of your slavery all the days of your life," says the *Torah*. Indeed, we are to "teach them diligently to your children," not because we are to fixate on the past or to wallow in our sorrow, but because we are to speak out in the face of the evil and suffering in our day.

Christians and Jews view this sorrow through entirely different lenses. I once compared my greatest childhood fears and most frightening nightmares with those of a Christian friend. His were waking up in the middle of the night, afraid his mother was raptured and saved from hell and he was not. I, in contrast, never once dreamed of heaven or hell, salvation or sin. But I do remember, and with great clarity, my recurring childhood dream of being alive during the Inquisition and forced to choose between converting to Christianity or being killed. The haunting images of the Holocaust, the crusades, the gallows, and the gas chamber—being martyred as a Jew for refusing to renounce my faith—these were my childhood nightmares, and, I dare say, those of many other Jews.

Is it at all possible for two communities with such divergent subliminal fears and dreams to ever come together as friends? Can Jews' most basic mistrust of Christians ever be overcome? Must "never forget" also mean "never forgive"?

יְהוָֹה

Many Christian pilgrim groups do not visit Yad Vashem. They'll visit the holy Christian sites and walk where Jesus walked. But they seldom come to this sacred place to remember what happened to their lord's people, to know what would have happened to their lord, Jesus the Jew, himself, had he been living in Europe in 1942.

Those Christians will never comprehend Israel or understand the Jewish people. Nor will they fully grasp Jews' insecurities and suspicious attitudes toward them. Much as they might try to identify with the Jewish roots of their own Christian faith, they will ultimately not succeed. For there is no coming to Jerusalem without traversing this road, paved over with the ashes of Auschwitz and Buchenwald and Treblinka. There is no reconciliation and healing between Christians and Jews, nor a reclamation of the integrity of the Christian witness, without acknowledging that while Christianity may not have directly caused the Holocaust, the long history of Christian anti-Semitism certainly provided the fertile seedbed within which that cataclysmic event could occur. The Holocaust did not erupt in a vacuum. It occurred, in no small measure, because of centuries of Christian persecution of Jews in the name of their Jewish lord, Jesus. Christians ought to be coming here en masse. It ought to be among the first places they visit in Israel. They, too, need to hear the message—and learn the lesson—never to forget.

יְהוָה

Jamie and I walked toward the main building of the Holocaust museum on the path known as the Avenue of the Righteous Gentiles. Rows of trees are planted on the sides of the road honoring or memorializing those courageous non-Jews who risked, and sometimes gave up, their lives to save Jews. The families of those modern-day saints are brought to Israel for the tree-planting ceremony, along with the Jews they saved.

Studies have found no discernable pattern of what kind of person was more likely to save Jews. There is no single character or background profile that identifies an individual as prone to risking his life to save another's. Some were motivated by friendship, others by Christian faith, still others by purely humanitarian impulses. More often than not, people saved Jews because "it was simply the right thing to do." Each time I come here, I ask myself, if the situation were reversed, would I be willing to risk my life and the life of my family to save others? I pray that I will never be put to that ultimate test.

יְהוָה

We looked around and saw a group of Japanese tourists led by a guide explaining in Japanese the meaning of this site. An old Jewish woman sat alone under a tree, crying, reading what appeared to be a letter. I wondered, did she survive the concentration camps? Could that letter be the last one written to her by her murdered husband? Parent? Young lover? What story did she have to tell? What did she bear witness to?

Jamie and I walked in silence down the Avenue of the Righteous, he a Christian, I a Jew, seeing the same trees but, I'm sure, experiencing this walk quite differently. We read the signs in front of the trees: HALINA KORZENIEWSKA, POLAND. TODOR AND PANDORA HADJI MITKOV, YUGOSLAVIA. OSCAR SCHINDLER, GERMANY. LUDWIG HENCEL, POLAND. EELKJENLTENTINK DE BOER, HOLLAND. SIJKE GORTER, HOLLAND. LEON PLATTEAU, BELGIUM. RAUL WALLENBERG, SWEDEN. CORRIE TEN BOOM, HOLLAND. Dozens of trees are planted, perhaps hundreds, but, tragically, not a forest.

We continued walking down the avenue, deep in thought, until Jamie broke the silence.

"Where was God when all this happened?" he asked.

I hesitated momentarily to respond to such a trite, yet sincerely profound, question.

"Where was man?" I finally responded. "God's copartner in the world was, for the most part, absent. That is why these trees are so important. They remind us of the goodness inherent in mankind. They give us hope in the face of despair. They redeem man and God—at least partially."

What I did not add, but what I was certainly thinking, was whether we Jews can ultimately rely on the goodness of a few saints, especially since I could not be certain I would come to the aid of another group which was threatened.

We passed a tree with a marker: FOR THE PEOPLE OF DENMARK. The Danes were one of the few nations that tried to save its Jewish population. When tipped off about the impending Nazi assault, they clandestinely transferred at night almost the entire Jewish community by boat to Sweden. Some Danish rescuers were, unfortunately, caught and killed.

We touched the exhibit boat, one of the actual ones used by the Danes to transport the Jews across the channel. It is a tiny boat that could seat four, maybe five people. When I had visited a few years earlier with my little daughter, she had asked the innocent but haunting question, "Abba, why aren't there more boats?"

The Jewish people will forever remember, with awesome gratitude, the sacrifice of those righteous gentiles. They renew our faith in God and in man. They help us from sinking into despair and from adopting a totally cynical view of the world. They remind us of the spark of the divine inherent in all creation.

And yet I, like millions of others, ask whether it is possible to believe in God after Auschwitz. In man?

"What does *Yad Vashem* mean?" Jamie asked, pointing to the sign overlooking the main building.

"It's a reference to a verse from the Bible: 'I will give them, in My house and within My walls, a monument and a name better than sons or daughters. I will give them an everlasting name which shall not perish.'"

We continued walking down the avenue and saw two young teenage Hassidim, sweating in the summer heat under their black hats and long heavy garb. Yesterday, on *Shabbat* in Meah Shearim, they had seemed to fit in so naturally to the surroundings. Here, they seemed so out of place.

The Holocaust, or *Shoah* as it is called in Hebrew, destroyed one-third of the Jewish people, eradicating roughly ninety percent of the Orthodox Jewish community of Europe, as well as their religious institutions—yeshivas, synagogues, and rabbis. Religious Jewish life as a whole was nearly destroyed. That it has revived powerfully in Israel and America—and that Jews have been able to flourish again after such a life-threatening blow—is nothing short of a miracle.

יהוה

Jamie and I entered the Hall of Remembrance, a simple edifice shaped like a bunker. Save for the flickering eternal flame, it is dark and somber inside. On the floor, in large letters, are the names of the concentration camps—DACHAU,

BURGEN-BELZEN, AUSCHWITZ, MAJDANEK—with wreaths lying next to them.

A group of elderly French Jews were gathered ahead of us, reciting the traditional *kel maleh rachamim* memorial prayers. They were Holocaust survivors, overwhelmed by memories. One of the men was crying. The pain and anguish they felt from the suffering they endured over half a century ago seemed as fresh and raw for them today as it was then.

I was suddenly struck by the fact that just a few days ago, while visiting the Wall, I had cried too. But in contrast to their tears, mine were of joy and thanksgiving to God for granting me the privilege of returning safely to Jerusalem. I prayed that their visit would comfort them with the balm of Gilead. An eerie silence pervaded the Hall of Remembrance as a cantor from the group chanted a prayer.

"What does that prayer mean?" Jamie asked.

"It is a plea to God to give the souls of the departed eternal rest, to hear the cries of the children and the elderly and never to forget the suffering we endured and never to abandon us again."

The smoke from the eternal flame rose up an open chimney, a powerful symbolic reminder of the crematoriums that belched smoke and ashes from the victims' bodies. Or perhaps a metaphor for the sacrifice offered in the ancient Temple that was totally consumed.

The cantor recited the *Kaddish*, the traditional Jewish prayer for the dead. *"Yisgadal viyiskadash shmay rabah."* May God's name be hallowed and sanctified in the world.

"I'm familiar with the *Mourner's Kaddish*," Jamie said, "but what does it mean?"

"It does not actually speak of death at all," I said. "It speaks of the sanctity of God's presence in the world and of our duty to step in the gap that has been left by the death of the departed and our pledge to sanctify God's name by filling the world with holiness.

One of the elderly French Jews placed a wreath next to the name of the concentration camp that the group had apparently endured and survived. The cantor softly sang the *Ani Maamin* prayer: "I believe in perfect faith in the coming of messiah. And even though he may tarry, nevertheless, I will continue to believe in him."

"Somehow," I explained, "Jews were able to find the courage and faith to walk to their deaths in the gas chambers with the words of this prayer of hope on their lips. In spite of the hopelessness of their situation—then and perhaps even today—Jews have been able to transcend the logical, surmount the impossible, and still hold on to the belief in the coming of messiah, world peace, and redemption of mankind.

יְהֹוָה

A group behind us speaking German was waiting to enter the hall, and I become agitated. A part of me wanted to scream out, "You did this," but I know that is not true. They, along with millions of other European non-Jews, come here to mourn, to remember, and to never forget. Americans, in contrast, seemed to have a more difficult time identifying with the cataclysmic events of World War II, perhaps because they have a weaker sense of history and were less directly affected by the war than the Europeans. All the more reason for them to visit this site. I wondered what those Germans were thinking and feeling, and I wondered what they or their parents did during the War.

Behind the Germans was a group of older Russians, and behind them, young Israeli soldiers in their crisp, olive-colored uniforms. The juxtaposition of those different people that were coming together in a shared mission and spirit to mourn and learn from the past, and to forge a better future, inspired me deeply.

יהוה

We left the Memorial Hall and walked past a series of striking sculptures. One of them depicted human bodies caught up in a barbed-wire fence. Another one showed a couple sheltering a mother and her child, marked: FOR THE UNKNOWN RIGHTEOUS AMONG THE NATIONS.

We worked our way toward the main building. "What is that over there?" Jamie asked, pointing.

"You'll see that everywhere in Israel," I replied. "It's a bomb shelter, in case we come under attack. By law, every public building in Israel must have one."

Jamie had been stoic and professional until then, almost strangely emotionally detached. But for some reason the bomb shelter got to him. He covered his face, broke down, and wept.

"When will they stop trying to destroy you? When will they ever just let you Jews live?"

The Talmud teaches that "there are those who acquire their place in heaven in one instant." In that moment, Jamie had fully grasped the burdens and pains of Jewish history.

"Today," he said tearfully, "I understand the cross of Jewish existence, and I declare that I will carry it with you as my own." He a Christian, I a Jew, despite our different faiths, backgrounds, and experiences, even the metaphors we use to describe our pain, through God's love, had become one. I began crying with him. Through wrenching tears we embraced each other as brothers.

We reached the main building of Yad Vashem. In the entrance was a large statue of Job. How appropriate. We visited the art exhibit section that displayed paintings and drawings made by children and adults during the Holocaust. Some of the works depicted life in the ghettos; others, depicted what life was like before the Nazi onslaught. One, in particular, caught my eye. It was a painting of beautiful sunflowers drawn by a young girl who survived the war and was living in Israel.

"I cannot comprehend how these people were able to preserve their humanity and creative spirit in such torturous times," said Jamie with a sigh. "It's comforting and redemptive that this was preserved here to bear testimony for generations."

יהוה

We passed a pile of children's shoes—hundreds of them—with a sign above it: ALL THAT REMAINED. A million and a half Jewish children perished in the Holocaust. In fact, they were the first group slated for extermination in the "final solution of the Jewish problem."

Walking silently side by side, Jamie and I came to a powerful painting that stood out among all the others. Titled *A Dream*, it shows a child being led out of a concentration camp by an angel. The child who painted it died in the camps. It was a dream that was not to be.

A young woman passing by gazed solemnly at the painting and broke down in tears. Immediately, everyone else in the room cried, including the macho Israeli soldier standing with his gun a few yards away. I don't know who that woman was—Jewish or Christian, Israeli or European. But with her simple act of weeping, she succeeded in bringing everyone in that room—strangers to one another—

together. All our differences dissolved in that instant of grief, in the shared oneness of our mourning. We were united in having caught a glimpse of human evil and suffering at their most base levels, in being witnesses to man's inhumanity to his fellow man in its most horrific, its darkest form.

"It's sad that we can't feel that same oneness outside this place." Jamie sighed.

יהוה

We passed another portrait showing Jews walking in a line into the camps. The inscription: BEHOLD THE LORD OF ISRAEL NEITHER SLUMBERS NOR SLEEPS. I wondered, was that an affirmation of faith or an act of protest?

We passed a portrait of a Nazi pulling Jesus down from the cross and sending him into line with the other Jews walking to Auschwitz. Jamie stood there mesmerized, not flinching for what must have been five minutes. Neither the picture nor his reaction needed explanation.

We passed a painting of a man killing himself on the electrified fence that surrounded the camps. Superimposed on the canvas were broken pieces of wood from a wooden fence forming the shape of a cross. The cross, symbol of the Christian faith par excellence and ultimate embodiment of God's love, was shattered, too, in the camps. Indeed, the Holocaust posed as much a challenge to Christians and Christianity, and to the integrity of the Christian witness, as it did to Jews and Judaism, perhaps even more so.

Jamie and I left the art exhibit hall and walked over to the Hall of Names, which contained ritual objects that were retrieved from Jewish communities destroyed in the Holocaust. A group of young Israeli soldiers guided by a slender, blond, female instructor was ahead of us. Jews from all over the world check the computerized database for information on their lost relatives. Over two million names are registered at Yad Vashem. Many are already entered in the computer data bank, and some are still listed in books piled up on tables—rows upon rows of them—laid out like coffins.

The army instructor suggested that perhaps these books are the only eulogy the Jews received. The young recruits listened attentively, hanging on her every word. One of the soldiers asked if he could use the computer to learn about what happened to his family that was destroyed in the shoah.

"Of course," she replied, "that's why it's here."

We passed another exhibit showing a black tomb. The inscription: POLAND 3,000,000, ITALY 15,000, GREECE 60,000, FRANCE 90,000, ROMANIA 295,000, CHILDREN 1,500,000...

Two feet away was a large sign: THE JEWISH PEOPLE WILL NEVER FORGET THE RIGHTEOUS AMONG THE NATIONS WHO ENDANGERED THEIR LIVES IN ORDER TO SAVE JEWS FROM THE NAZI MURDERERS AND THEIR COLLABORATORS. IN THEIR PRAISEWORTHY DEEDS, THEY SAVED THE HONOR OF MANKIND.

"I'm really moved," said Jamie, "by all the tributes here to non-Jewish rescuers."

"It's genuine and heartfelt," I responded. "Jewish people have made a sacred oath, never to forget the evil and never to forget the sparks of goodness inherent in all of humanity."

As we continued our tour, I got the distinct impression that Israelis believe that, with the establishment of the State of Israel, a holocaust of Jews could never happen again. It's not so much hubris on their part as sheer determination that prompts them to believe that. Today, in sharp contrast with 1940, Jews have a place to flee. Indeed, when Jews were threatened in far-off Uganda, the Israeli Air Force flew thousands of miles to pluck them out of danger and save them from disaster. Jews the world over rely on the fact that there is a strong Jewish army, the Israeli Defense Forces, that will protect us from danger and save us from despair, wherever we may be.

יהוה

We entered a large hall with a sign running across the entire length of the wall. It was a quote from *Anne Frank: The Diary of a Young Girl*: WHO HAS INFLICTED THIS UPON US? WHO HAS MADE US JEWS DIFFERENT FROM OTHER PEOPLE?

Another wall carried a different sign: REMEMBER THAT WHICH AMALEK DID TO US, REMEMBER EVERYTHING. DO NOT FORGET FOR THE REST OF YOUR LIVES AND PASS THIS ON AS A HOLY TESTAMENT TO THE COMING GENERATIONS.

יהוה

The Holocaust did not erupt suddenly and with no warning. It came about in a series of stages. The museum depicts each, with its own exhibit: The period from 1933 to 1939, the anti-Jewish policy in Germany; from 1939 to 1941, the establishment of ghettos; from 1941 to 1945, mass murder; from 1945 forward, the liberation and aftermath. And while there was Jewish resistance in different forms throughout these periods, the pinnacle was the Warsaw Ghetto uprising in 1943, which is also depicted here.

The first exhibit portrays German Jewry before 1933 and is followed by the rise and consolidation of power of the Nazis. Photos of books being burned are displayed with this inscription: WHERE BOOKS ARE BURNED, HUMAN BEINGS ARE ALSO DESTINED TO BE BURNED. HEINRICH HEINE, 1820.

יהוה

Jamie and I watched a movie depicting Jewish life in Eastern Europe before the Nazi rise, and we learned of the anti-Jewish measures enacted in the period from 1933 to 1938, effectively separating Jews from the rest of society.

"It's sad that that whole world and culture is virtually gone," I said.

"I'm glad I caught a glimpse of it yesterday at the Hassidic tisch," said Jamie.

The world's response to these horrific events was shown next. We read how ships filled with Jewish refugees, desperately trying to escape the coming onslaught, were turned back at ports around the world, including the United States.

Finally, we came to the exhibit on the Warsaw Ghetto. Eighty-five thousand Jews died there, including twenty thousand children. We passed pictures of children lying in the street, some dead, others begging for a morsel of bread. We read the explanation on the wall:

March 7, 1942.

The bodies are separated into three categories. In the first are those brought to the cemetery purification room. The second consists of the bodies that were cleansed in their own homes. They are the fortunate ones who receive a halfway decent burial—nowadays that is a considerable privilege. The third classification includes all those who died of starvation or the epidemics—they are the majority! These bodies are put into a common grave, just as they were picked up: naked and unwashed. Dozens upon dozens of such corpses are accumulated each day in the cemetery stables to await their burial at sunrise. A thin layer of earth is spread over the burial pit, but not in sufficient quantity to cover the limbs.

From the Warsaw Diary
of Chaim Kaplan.

The army instructor in front of us was pointing to a photo showing people walking past young children begging for food. The soldiers were uncomfortable, even angry, and the instructor sensed that. "We cannot judge them," she said to her recruits. "Who knows what we would have done in the same situation?"

We saw a photo of Hassidim crowded around the table, just as Jamie and I had been last night, singing and listening to the Rebbe. The synagogue looked amazingly similar to the one we had been in. "The Jewish people have survived all this and rebuilt their lives of faith," Jamie said. "I saw it yesterday with my own eyes."

And then we came to a haunting photo—a Nazi pointing a rifle at a naked Jewish woman holding her child, trying to protect him from the bullets. She is standing hunched over at the edge of a ditch, with her back toward the Nazi. He is standing just a few feet away, at point-blank range, about to shoot her and her child. The sign above the photo with a quote from a German engineer, an eyewitness to the murder of the Jews of Dubno in October 1942 reads:

The people got off the lorries—men, women, and children of all ages—were forced to strip by order of an SS wielding horse whip or dog whip. The people undressed without a cry or tear, stood together, family by family, kissed each other and said goodbye... During the fifteen minutes I stood near the trench, I did not hear a single complaint or plea for mercy. I looked at a family of about eight people: a man and his wife both about fifty with children with them, aged one, eight, and ten, and two grown-up daughters, aged twenty and twenty-four. An old woman with snow-white hair held the year-old child in her arms singing to it and tickling it. The father held the hand of the boy of about ten and spoke to him gently. The child tried to keep back his tears. The father pointed toward heaven and stroked the child's head and appeared to be explaining something to him. The SS man counted about twenty people and ordered them to go to the side of the heap of earth, among them were the family I had described... The trench was already about two-thirds full. I estimated that it held about 1,000 people. I observed the man who was shooting. He was an SS man who sat on the edge of the trench on its narrow side with his legs dangling inside it. His submachine gun was on his knees and he was smoking a cigarette.

Jamie and I moved on, difficult as it was, gazing at photos of the cattle trains that carried Jews to their death. Next we saw pictures of them arriving at the camps, standing in line for the selection process. There it was determined, by the flick of a hand, who would live—at least for a while and endure gruesome labor—and who would die immediately in the gas chambers and crematoriums.

Most Jews never gave up hope in their survival until the very end, when it was too late for either hope or action. After all, they imagined, what possible purpose would it serve the Nazis to kill them? Surely they would be sent to labor camps to work for the Nazi war machine, not exterminated. And certainly human beings, even Nazis, wouldn't do such a thing to them for no reason other than that they were Jews. And certainly the world wouldn't allow such a thing to happen. So the Jews believed.

We walked through a small dark tunnel symbolizing the underground sewers Jews in the Warsaw Ghetto used in their attempts to escape. We came to another series of photos with this sign: GOLD TEETH EXTRACTED FROM THE CORPSES WERE MELTED INTO BARS BY SS DOCTORS... HAIR WAS SENT TO A CERTAIN FACTORY IN BAVARIA TO BE USED FOR THE ARMS INDUSTRY.

We overheard the Israeli army guide explaining to her group how the Muslim mufti of Jerusalem secretly met with the Nazis and planned to destroy the Jews of Palestine should the Nazis invade there, which they came dangerously close to doing. If given the chance, most Arabs today would have no hesitation to do likewise, she continued.

"Is she paranoid," asked Jamie, "or just trying to brainwash her recruits with propaganda? I really don't believe the Arabs harbor genocidal plans against Jews."

"Could it be," I said, pointing to the exhibits, "that we Jews have good reason to be paranoid?"

The guide continued telling the young soldiers that Jews need to be vigilant to the eruption of anti-Semitism even today. "We must never forget what happened in Europe to our parents and grandparents."

She allowed her troops a brief moment of quiet in which to gather their thoughts. Then she added softly, in her beautiful Hebrew, these gripping words that the six million Holocaust victims never heard: "And, if necessary, we must be prepared to act on behalf of Jews who are threatened anywhere and everywhere. *Am Yisrael Chai*, the people of Israel lives... *viyichyeh,* and shall live."

Photos from 1948 ended the exhibit. The photos illustrated the birth of the State of Israel, and poignantly intimated that until Jews had a safe haven and home of their own to flee to, the Holocaust did not really come to an end. The sad and horrible truth is that even after the war was over and the bewildered and forlorn remnants of the Jewish people sought to make their way to Palestine, the British, who controlled the country at the time, denied entry to them. Those who were caught trying to break through the blockade were sent to displaced persons camps in Cyprus where they remained for as long as three years. Even more, a few years *after* the war, thousands of Jews who had survived the Holocaust and returned to their old homes in Poland to begin their lives anew were subjected to a horrible anti-Semitic pogrom in which hundreds were killed. This outburst prompted most of the remaining Jews to leave for good. It had become eminently clear that, contrary to Jews' expectations, the diabolical forces of anti-Semitism had not, in fact, been expunged.

יהוה

As we exited the museum, we passed one final sign hanging over the doorway: FORGETFULNESS LEADS TO EXILE, WHILE REMEMBRANCE IS THE SECRET OF REDEMPTION. BAAL SHEM TOV.

It is tremendously uplifting to see young Israeli soldiers touring Yad Vashem. This is especially true of Sephardic and Ethiopian Jews whose families were untouched by the Holocaust, which affected only European Ashekenazic Jews. It's also reassuring to see tough Israeli soldiers, tears welling in their eyes, collectively declaring the sacred Jewish vow, never to forget.

The museum is a sobering and humbling antidote to youthful cockiness. The new generation of Israelis must be strong and ever vigilant. But they must also know that Jews remain vulnerable and that the IDF is not invincible. And they must accept the responsibility placed on their shoulders, to protect the Jewish people whenever and wherever they are threatened.

יְהֹוָה

We made our way out of the main building and walked over to the Children's Memorial site, the final exhibit in the Yad Vashem complex, and certainly the most architecturally challenging. How do you create a memorial that does justice to the murder of a million and a half children?

Jamie and I entered the bunkerlike exhibit and were thrust into pitch-darkness. We immediately became disoriented and insecure in our step. We groped to find the side rail to steady us, give us direction, and prevent us from stumbling. It seemed like thousands of tiny candles were piercing the darkened hall, though in reality only a single candle, reflected through dozens of mirrors, lay at the center of the room. Flashing around us were images of children who perished in the Holocaust. The room was silent, save for the haunting soft strains of music and the names of children being recited, one every three seconds. We instinctively tried to turn back, but we could not find our way in the dark maze. We pressed forward into the darkness.

SHALOM NOVITCH, FOUR YEARS OLD, POLAND. BRUNO UMNOVITCH, NINE YEARS OLD, HOLLAND... The names and images of children enveloped us. We struggled to breathe.

And then, suddenly, it was over. We exited a doorway, gasped for air, and adjusted our eyes to the bright sunlight. The powerful experience had overwhelmed everyone walking out of the exhibit. No one spoke. We all walked slower than when we went in. Most were standing still, emotionally paralyzed by this simple monument to children, the single candle piercing the darkness, awesome in its simplicity and profundity.

We gazed at the beautiful panorama of the Judean Hills and city of Jerusalem. The landscape was a warm comfort to our fractured souls. From afar, we saw a group of American teenagers leaving the Memorial Hall we had visited earlier, proudly singing the Israeli national anthem, "Hatikvah." Hope. The words of the prophet inspired my spirit: "For there is a reward for your labor—declares the LORD: [Your children] shall return from the enemy's land. And there is hope for your future—declares the LORD: Your children shall return to their country." Indeed, they have.

יהוה

Experiencing Yad Vashem together, Jamie viewing it as refracted through his Christian lens and me through my Jewish one, brought us together in a special way. For the second time in just a few days, our tears had comingled. Our tears of joy in visiting the Kotel had given way to those of sadness as we faced the epitome of man's inhumanity toward his fellow man. We had come to Jerusalem with separate agendas and different expectations. But we had now walked together on the dark road traversing Auschwitz, Buchenwald, and Treblinka. And we had basked together in the warm sunshine and radiant beauty of the vibrant city of Jerusalem.

CHAPTER ELEVEN

MOVNT HERZL CEMETERY

"Would you like a ride?" asked the army guide in perfect English.

"Thanks, but no thanks," I quickly said, much to Jamie's chagrin. "There is one more spot we must visit."

I explained to Jamie that we were just a few minutes walk from Mount Herzl, the military cemetery where those who died defending the State of Israel are buried—Israeli's Arlington Cemetery, if you will. Theodore Herzl, founder of modern political Zionism and father of the new Jewish nation is also buried there.

"It's important for us to acknowledge our debt to those who paid the ultimate price so that you and I could walk carefree throughout this beautiful land."

"Okay," Jamie said, as he watched the beautiful Israeli army guide board the bus. "But can I at least get her phone number?"

We took a short break for washrooms and a cup of coffee, and walked over to Mount Herzl.

As we reached the entrance, we saw a group of elderly Russian Jewish immigrants, war heroes from the former

Soviet Union, standing proudly in their Soviet uniforms, basking in the Jerusalem sunlight.

I wondered what they were thinking at that moment. Whether they did the right thing by leaving their home-land, mother Russia? Or perhaps the opposite, why they risked their lives fighting for their Communist nation, only to suffer persecution and religious oppression at its hands later on? Those elderly Soviet Jews, regaled with big bulky medals hanging from their lapels and seeming to weigh them down, appeared so out of place here.

The young Israeli soldiers stared at them, and I won-dered what was going through their minds. Perhaps they were trying to comprehend why those Jews had risked their lives fighting for a foreign nation that later mis-treated them so grievously? Or perhaps they were won-dering why those old men refused to let go of their shattered dreams and diaspora past, and why they didn't instead embrace their new reality and celebrate their liv-ing freely as Jews in a Jewish state.

At the grave of Herzl, I thought it appropriate to tell Jamie that when Theodore Herzl organized the first World Zionist Congress in Basel, Switzerland, in 1897, he declared that in five years, perhaps fifty, a Jewish state would be born. Almost prophetically, the Jewish state was established fifty-one years later. Dreamer? Lunatic? Pragmatist? Statesman? Whatever the case, Herzl reinstilled in the hearts of the Jewish people a spirit of Zionism—that age-old Jewish dream to return to their ancient homeland, Israel—and a commitment to shape it in its new nationalistic and political form. While Zionism was not a new idea—after all, the Bible speaks of a Jewish return to Zion repeatedly, a dream that was kept alive over the centuries—Herzl was the father of its contemporary political expression. His motto was, If you will it, it is no dream.

Herzl was an assimilated Austrian journalist sent by his newspaper to cover the Dreyfus trial then being held in France. Captain Dreyfus, a Jew, was accused of the trumped-up charge of sedition and was found guilty by a kangaroo court. But it was the bloodcurdling cries of "kill the Jews" shouted by people inside and outside the courtroom that jarred Herzl's sensibilities. The prevalence of anti-Semitism, and its apparent acceptability in modern "enlightened" France, convinced him that Jews would never succeed in eradicating the forces of bigotry unless they established a nation of their own. It was this incident that provoked him to launch the political movement that led to the establishment of the Jewish State in 1948.

יהוה

Jamie and I walked past some exquisite flowers exuding an almost sensual aroma. We stood together in a field of green grass interspersed with bunkers remaining from the War of Independence. The sound of F-14s flying overhead shattered the quiet.

We passed an old bunker dug into the mountain and surrounded by sandbags, another remnant of the 1948 war. I thought of how just a few years ago distraught mourners in Bosnia, even while burying their dead, were brutally attacked and slaughtered.

יהוה

The Jewish people have made a solemn vow never again to allow themselves to become vulnerable to the kinds of atrocities visited upon innocents in Bosnia, Rwanda, and Kosova—all *after* the world insisted it had learned the lesson of "never again." Israel has chosen to seize and wield power in a moral manner. And while power can, indeed, corrupt, and absolute power can corrupt absolutely, Jews have learned that absolute power*less*ness can corrupt even more.

There were two basic schools of Zionist thought at the turn of the century. The one led by Herzl viewed Israel, first and foremost, as a haven from oppression, a physical refuge to which Jews could flee in case of an outbreak of anti-Semitism. The second, led by the popular Yiddish writer Achad Haam, stressed that Israel is the cultural center of Jewish life and that this role is best summarized by the scriptural verse, "For instruction shall come forth from Zion, the word of the LORD from Jerusalem."

The two ideological forces clashed in 1903 when the Jews of Eastern Europe were experiencing horrible pogroms, especially in Kishinev, Poland. Herzl and many of the delegates attending the Zionist Congress that year were willing to accept the offer of Uganda as their new Jewish nation and haven to which the Jewish people could flee. Others rejected it in the belief that only Israel, land of the Bible, could serve as their national homeland. After much heated debate, the delegates opposing Herzl walked out of the assembly and brought passage of the Uganda proposal (and consideration of any land other than Israel) to an abrupt and irreversible end.

The inevitable implication of that watershed event was that the Jewish people would have to defend themselves against a hostile local Arab population and twenty-three Arab nations that rejected the idea of a Jewish state in their midst. The Jewish people had made the decision that only in *eretz yisrael*, land of their forefathers, could they fulfill their ancient Jewish dream and modern Zionist goal of rebuilding the Jewish nation.

We passed a section dedicated to the memory of those from the Israeli navy who died at sea without a burial. Instead of graves, there is a little pool of water with the names of the deceased inscribed on the sides and bottom: DAVID FOGEL, TWENTY-TWO; JOSEPH FRIEDLER, TWENTY-ONE; ISRAEL FELDMAN, TWENTY-FOUR...

We passed an old man praying and putting flowers on the water next to one of the names. Perhaps his son? Memories of the past permeated the air and continued to infuse the present with its trauma and sting.

יהוה

The Israeli people stand fully behind the Israel Defense Forces if only because here the people *are* the armed forces. But if ever, God forbid, the IDF were to become politicized, demoralized, or viewed by the citizens with cynicism or detachment, the nation could likely not survive. For the trust Jews place in the IDF is the most precious, cohesive factor binding together an otherwise deeply divided people. It is like Samson's hair, the secret source of their powerful strength. Because of the people's absolute trust in the moral integrity and professional capabilities of the IDF, the State and the people of Israel are enabled to survive against all odds and to withstand the many wars and sacrifices she has had to endure.

The graves are well kept, chiseled on the top with the name and age of the fallen soldier and a Star of David on top. Some are still fresh, from as recently as a few weeks ago. These Jews died as Jews, much like those memorialized a few yards away at Yad Vashem. But the chasm between the two sites is enormous. Unlike those whose martyrdom is sanctified at Yad Vashem, those buried here died, not as defenseless victims, but as proud free men fighting for their right to live as Jews in *eretz yisrael*. The fresh graves, security pits, and air raid shelters around us are stark reminders that this battle is not yet over.

יהוה

"It's painful to realize that more graves will, undoubtedly, be dug here, if not tomorrow, then the next day, or next month." Jamie sighed.

We walked a bit farther and came across the same group of Russian war heroes we had seen earlier. They were conducting a ceremony next to the monument memorializing members of the British and Russian-Jewish brigades who died fighting the Nazis in World War II. Never in their wildest dreams did those Russian Jews imagine that some fifty years after the war they would be living in Israel, laying a wreath for their dead Russian comrades in Israel's military cemetery. I was reminded of the verse from the Bible, "When the LORD restores the fortunes of Zion—we see it as in a dream."

יהוה

Emigrating to a new land is difficult enough with such challenges as leaving one's roots, severing one's relationship with friends and country, finding a new job, learning a new language, and making new friends. It's gratifying to see men come together to nostalgically embrace their past, even as they step carefully with hope toward their future.

In addition to the Russian and British Jews who died in WWII, the memorial commemorates those Jews who fought the Nazis with the British forces and later emigrated to Palestine, only to be killed there. Not surprisingly, those who survived the war became the military leaders of the new Jewish state. And since the British army had trained them, the Israeli Defense Forces modeled their strategy, uniforms, and tactics after them.

Israeli dignitaries, high-ranking army officials, Knesset members, and military police were participating in the ceremony honoring the former Soviet heroes. The juxtaposition of the Russian Jews and the young Israeli soldiers was striking. A new generation of Jews had emerged; the baton had been passed on.

The presence of the Soviet Jews in Israel corroborates the ubiquitous Israeli conviction that sooner or later all Jews will find themselves here. Israel will be the home of the resurrected Jewish people. Diaspora Jewish life today may very well be a relic of the past in its last throes of desperation, incapable of preserving Jewish continuity or of ensuring Jewish survival. The dream of "Hatikvah"—to be a free people in their *own* homeland—could very well shatter and supplant the secure dreams of so many Russian Jews who envisioned life in their fatherland.

I wonder whether this prevalent fatalistic Israeli view of the diaspora has merit, especially regarding the United States where Jews feel most comfortable and secure. But who would have believed just a few years ago that the walls of Communism would fall and the gates of the Soviet Union suddenly swing open to bring almost a million Jews to join this tiny young country's destiny? Who could have imagined then that a ceremony like this, led jointly by former Soviet war heroes and their young Israeli counterparts, would ever take place in Jerusalem? There has, indeed, been a definite shift from the diaspora to Israel for both the bearers and preservers of the Jewish destiny, a supplanting of one Jewish vision with another.

"You're American, right?" said an older Israeli to me and Jamie.

We nodded affirmatively.

"Don't think you can escape your Jewish destiny. You are doomed in America, just like those old Russian Jews over there," he said, pointing to the group at the monument. "Either anti-Semitism or assimilation will get you. Israel is the only answer. Have you ever asked yourself," he continued to my deep embarrassment, "why you Jews contribute so much to American society when you could be directing your creative energies toward building up the land of Israel for your own Jewish people?"

I was offended by his remarks—not so much because I thought they were out of line since I have frequently asked myself that very question—but because of the sensitive issue of dual loyalties. I was concerned about Jamie's reaction.

Sensing my uneasiness, Jamie turned to me reassuringly and said, "Don't worry, I'm cool. I realize that some of you see yourselves as American Jews and others as Jewish American. I also know the horrors you Jews have endured throughout history because of that noxious charge. Actually," he continued, almost as an afterthought, "I thought that man's question was a very challenging and reasonable one."

I thanked Jamie for his sensitivity. I explained how some Israelis are so disillusioned by life in Israel that they emigrate to the diaspora. Some wonder why American Jews even consider *aliyah*. Others cannot comprehend how a Jew could feel such great comfort in and allegiance to America, view it as *their* country, and *not* live in Israel.

"But we need you too," insisted Jamie. "If American Jews were to leave for Israel, how could the world benefit from your many achievements and contributions to society? Can you imagine life without the Salk vaccine? Einstein? Itzhak Perlman? Marc Chagall? Throughout history, those nations that sought to persecute their Jews suffered as a result and fell from grace in their culture, science, business, and power.

"I'd even give you a self-interest argument if the altruistic one isn't convincing," Jamie said, getting even more animated. "If Jews, who are so deeply involved in American politics and influential in public policy institutions, were to emigrate to Israel, do you really think the United States would continue to be the staunch friend to Israel she is? I'd like to believe the answer is yes, but I don't think so.

"I am not a Jew," Jamie went on, "but I can appreciate your concern with the threats that assimilation would pose to American Jewish survival. On the other hand, I wonder about those Jews—like that guy who came up to us a few minutes ago—who really believe an outbreak of anti-Semitism, let alone a holocaust, could happen in the U.S.

"And one more argument," Jamie said, taking a deep breath. "Aren't you Jews called upon to be a 'light unto nations' and to share your monotheistic vision of God and ethical living with us goyim? How can you fulfill that role if you all live in Israel? You gave us our Bible, our Lord, our spiritual heritage, even our moral codes. We need you Jews with us," Jamie said emphatically.

"And let me emulate you and my Lord Jesus by citing the biblical teaching that one day ten gentiles will grab the hem of a Jew and ask him to teach them of God's word. How will we learn from you if you are not in America with us?"

Normally, I would have smilingly responded to his query with "by Internet and satellite," but that would clearly have been out of place now.

"And one last thing that bothers me," he added to his passionate soliloquy. "Why do you feel so separate and different from the rest of us? Can't you get it into your mind that we accept you Jews in America? At this point, you're more a part of the establishment than us WASPs. You're not some marginal group of foreigners and aliens. Why do you Jews feel so insecure all the time? Why do you want to move away from us?"

I was deeply moved by Jamie's plea. The contrast between his attitude and past Christian attitudes toward Jews and their place in society struck me deeply. For two thousand years Jews were viewed as expendable. Virtually every European nation, at one time or another, sought to rid itself of its Jews, either by expulsion or extermination. And here was this gentile journalist passionately arguing why Jews should remain in America and, in fact, how much they are needed and wanted. I wondered if Jamie had had these views before he came to Israel a few days ago? Was he reflecting his own newly formed opinions or those of most Americans today? And if push came to shove and Jews in America were threatened, how many non-Jews would put their lives at risk to help them?

The fact is, I agreed with Jamie. Jews are accepted in America. Even appreciated. But so were the Jews in Germany. I wondered anew, are Jews in America tolerated or accepted? And given the right political and socioeconomic circumstances, could latent anti-Semitism find expression even in the U.S.?

"And finally," Jamie said, interrupting my thoughts.

"This is your third *finally*, Jamie," I interjected.

"No, this is truly my final, most compelling argument," Jamie said. "In this nuclear age, just one or two bombs could destroy all the Jewish people living here in Israel. How wise would it be for you Jews to put all your eggs in this one basket by living here in Israel? You need to spread the risk around."

"If, God forbid, the State of Israel were destroyed," I responded, "and the very thought of such a possibility is almost a sacrilege and beyond my comprehension, I doubt diaspora Jewish life could survive anyway. And frankly," I continued after some hesitation, "I'm not sure it should."

"Those are strong words, my friend," said Jamie.

"I know. But I believe they're true. I doubt we Jews could survive the trauma of another Holocaust. And I don't believe our Jewish faith could withstand the destruction of Israel. Jewish life is too tenuous and fragile to withstand such a life blow. What's more—and it may shock you that I say this—I don't see how we Jews could continue to believe in God after such a cataclysm. After all, what kind of God would allow another holocaust to occur?"

Jamie looked me straight in the eye and said almost defiantly, "But how would Israel's destruction be different, at least in terms of belief in God, from the annihilation of six million Jews in the 1940s? If you believe in God now, after the Holocaust, why would you stop believing in Him sixty years later, if another six million Jews would be destroyed? Are you suggesting it's possible to believe in a God who murders six million Jews but not twelve?"

"You know, Jamie," I said, dangerously close to anger, "I'm sorry. I just cannot talk about such things. Let's drop the subject."

The truth is, Jamie had touched on a tender nerve. After all, how can we believe in a God—who is omniscient, omnipotent, and merciful—and who allows even one innocent child to die? The Jobian theodicy problem of why the righteous suffer and the wicked prosper is as much an issue whether it is six million or twelve million or even just one innocent child who dies. And to that argument, I had no response.

An Israeli army chaplain chanted from the psalms and led the gathering in the *Mourner's Kaddish*. Despite decades of Soviet oppression when Jews were prohibited from studying Hebrew and practicing their Jewish faith, the last remaining vestige of Jews' awareness of their faith is the *Kaddish* memorial prayer.

Watching those hard-nosed, former Communist soldiers chanting the *Kaddish* reminded me of the rabbinic teaching that God brought the Jewish people out of Egypt at the last possible moment, after they had sunk to the forty-ninth level of impurity. Had he waited till they sunk just one more level, they would have been beyond redemption. Those Soviet Jews had forgotten everything from their faith. The last remaining spark they held on to, curiously enough, was the *Mourner's Kaddish*. Why, I wondered, did God always wait till the last possible moment—if at all—before interceding and plucking us from the fire, and redeeming us from disaster and despair? Doesn't he place too much trust in man and his ability to choose good over evil? Could we Jews be sorely mistaken in affirming a God who gives man freedom of choice, even to the point of allowing his creation to destroy one another? Could Christians, in fact, be right in insisting that man is inherently depraved, tainted by original sin? Is the Jewish view of the basic purity of man too noble and untenable a conviction?

יהוה

We walked among the graves: MICHAEL NAVOT, SON OF TAMAR AND TUVIA, BORN IN JERUSALEM, FELL DURING HIS TIME OF SERVICE, FIVE SHVAT 1948, NINETEEN YEARS OLD. DANIEL MENACHEM, TWENTY YEARS OLD WHEN HE FELL. SHOSHANA PERI, FELL IN JERUSALEM IN 1948, TWENTY YEARS OLD WHEN SHE FELL...

Wave upon wave of graves, row upon row of Stars of David. Jamie lingered, deep in thought.

"It's time to move on," I said, "literally and figuratively. We've prayed at the Wall, we've cried at Yad Vashem, and we've mourned here at the military cemetery. It's time to start our tour of Israel."

Jamie didn't do anything that indicated he even heard me. He was lost in thought.

I decided to gamble with his emotions.

"Hey, Jamie, did you hear the one about the elderly Jewish patient being treated at Mount Sinai Hospital? He kept asking to be moved to Saint Joseph Hospital a few miles away. A nurse asked him why he wanted to be transferred. 'Aren't the doctors here good?' she asked.

"'Excellent, I can't complain,' the patient said.

"'And how about the food and nursing staff? Aren't they satisfactory?'

"'Excellent, I can't complain,' he said.

"'Then why do you want to go to Saint Joseph's?' asked the sweet nurse.

"'Oh, because *there* I can complain,' the old patient said.

"Get it? Jamie, there he could complain!"

Jamie remained silent. He was clearly not ready to move on. And that was fine. Christians—and Jews—need their space to think and pray after visiting these two traumatic sites. We Jews ought not place a guilt trip on Christians, as if they were somehow responsible for the slaughter. Such actions are not only morally wrong and psychologically debilitating, they will, ultimately, backfire by leading to feelings of anger and hostility toward Jews. To be sure, Jamie needed to face up to the Holocaust and confront it, as we all do. He also needed to express his feelings and talk about it, but all in due time. And now was, apparently, not yet the time.

As we left Mount Herzl, we saw a group of children playing in a nearby park. "That's our response to the
Holocaust," I said, pointing to the children.

"*Am Yisrael chai viyichye,*" answered Jamie. The people of
Israel lives and shall live."

יהוה

We boarded a public bus and quickly sat down. "*Rega!
Rega!*" suddenly screamed half the bus. "Wait! Wait!"
Apparently, an old woman was still getting off the bus from
the back door as the bus had begun moving. Fortunately,
the driver stopped and no one was hurt.

"You see," I said, turning to Jamie, "that's one of the traits
I admire most about Israelis."

"What do you mean?" answered Jamie, who was now in
better humor. "The fact that the bus drivers are incompe-
tent?"

"No," I said, "the fact that Israelis are not too shy, embarrassed, inhibited, or intimidated to stand out in a crowd
and assist others. They feel at home here, not disengaged
from one another as we in America often feel. If a person
needs help, they get involved.

"Do you remember the episode of Kitty Genovese, the
woman who was raped, stabbed, and left to die while
twenty-three people stood by, refusing to even call the
police? That will forever be etched in my mind. I doubt that
could happen here in Israel. Here people feel like family
toward one another and act accordingly without pretense
or encumbrance by politically correct niceties. In Israel, you
get what you see—for the good or bad. Sure, Israelis have
rough edges. But the spirit of genuineness is so attractive
and refreshing that it prompts even foreigners to feel comfortable and uninhibited here."

"America was probably like that, too, in its early formative years," said Jamie. "The question I have is whether this characteristic of Israeli society can be maintained as the population becomes larger and ethnically divergent and as technology leads to greater depersonalization and detachment."

"You're right," I said.

"Hopefully," Jamie added, "this downright chutzpa Israelis exhibit is never lost."

"I'll say *amen* to that, brother."

יהוה

"What are those barrels on top of the houses?" Jamie asked, pointing out the taxi window toward an apartment complex nearby.

"They're called *dudei shemesh*, Jamie, an Israeli invention that provides much of the country with solar energy. In fact, Israel has become one of the world's pioneers in the field of solar energy. Water accumulates in the barrels and is warmed by the sun's reflection on attached mirrors. And since there is no oil to speak of here, and Israel does not want to be dependent upon foreign sources of energy that can be turned on and off without provocation, most homes get their hot water in this way.

"Hey," I said, trying once more to introduce a little levity, "did you hear the one about why it took the Israelites forty years of wandering through the desert before they reached Israel? They were looking for the one place in the Middle East without oil."

"Well, they certainly found it," replied Jamie.

A woman who overheard my feeble attempt at humor—which was actually a joke first told by the late Golda Meir—interjected, "No, that's not why. It's men. You know, they just won't stop to ask for directions."

We chuckled, not only at her humor but that she felt comfortable enough to intrude on our private conversation—typically Israeli.

"I remember reading once in the *Wall Street Journal*," said Jamie, "about a group of Christians who were digging for oil on the basis of a prophecy in the Bible that says of the tribe of Dan, 'They shall dip their feet in oil.'"

"Very good," I said. "Except for one thing. The oral tradition of Judaism interprets that verse as referring to *olive* oil. But look at how far Israel is willing to go for the sake of peace. Just a few years ago, she gave to Egypt all the oil wells she had discovered in Sinai, even those excavated at her own expense. She sacrificed her energy independence and became reliant upon foreign sources of fuel, all for the sake of the *possibility* of peace."

"Does the world have any idea how far this nation is willing to go for peace?" asked Jamie. "Or any appreciation for it?"

יהוה

I grinned, bemused. Jamie was becoming a right wing Likud party provocateur. Americans tend to be politically naive about the Arab world, particularly its intentions vis-à-vis Israel, and its regard for Western values as a whole. While there are, to be sure, fundamental differences among the Arab nations in their willingness to accept Israel's existence, as Abba Eban, the dovish leader once said, the Arabs never miss the opportunity to miss the opportunity for peace, in contrast to Israel, which has repeatedly demonstrated such a willingness.

Why should Israel feel morally pressured by oil-rich reactionary countries like Saudi Arabia, which treats women like chattel and deprives their citizens of the most basic freedoms? Even the simple act of conducting non-Muslim prayer services is expressly prohibited in these Western-oriented Arab nations.

And how shall we comprehend the Arab willingness to send their young children to do battle with Israeli soldiers as they did in the intifada? Since they, undoubtedly, care about their children as we Jews do, could it be that they rely upon Jewish soldiers' humane values and loathing to kill children even at their own risk? Does it stand in stark contrast with the Israelis' conviction to protect their children and even die in their place?

The values and ethos of Arabs and Israelis are fundamentally different, though many naive, well-intentioned liberals are loath to admit it. When it comes to the Arab-Israeli conflict, many Westerners project their own tolerant values onto the Arab world and adopt a moral equivalence between the two groups. Many also assume a double standard in relation to Israel, expecting more from her than from Arab nations. I wonder, do such expectations stem from prejudice toward Jews or out of a belief in the moral superiority of Jews?

יְהוָה

We got off at the center of town, bought a falafel, and sat down to eat it on a bench in the pedestrian mall. An awkward quiet still existed between us, notwithstanding my attempts to move on with corny humor. The emotional pull of Yad Vashem and Mount Herzl was not easily dislodged.

"Now I understand," Jamie said suddenly, breaking the silence.

"Understand what?" I asked.

"I finally understand everything, why you Jews are the way you are, why Israeli politicians are the way they are, why sometimes you guys seem so paranoid and insecure, so strident, arrogant, and downright stubborn. And yet, a part of me doesn't understand anything at all."

"Welcome to Israel, Jamie," I answered. "Like everyone else here, you think you know everything but realize you know nothing."

I once had a rabbi who explained to me that there are four levels of knowledge—the lowest level is knowing nothing. The level above that is knowing a little. The level above that is knowing everything. The fourth and highest level is realizing you know nothing.

Instead of filling us up, the falafel just whetted our appetite.

"I'm hungry," I said.

"And I could use a stiff drink," responded Jamie, chuckling. "Let's go someplace different," I said, as we walked to my favorite Yemenite restaurant.

"Always interested in trying new cuisine," said Jamie, with a note of sarcasm in his voice.

We sat down in a corner booth.

"I'll have a cheeseburger," Jamie said with a straight face to the waitress, a beautiful, slender Yemenite girl with dark, exotic features.

"I'm sorry, sir," she responded in broken English. "We don't serve that here. We only serve Yemenite food."

"Why don't you put together a selection of items you think my American friend here might enjoy," I suggested. "Give him a taste of good old-fashioned Yemenite food."

Jamie was being very friendly to her. Too friendly.

"Are you spoken for?" he asked the waitress.

"I'm sorry; I not understand," she said.

"Never mind," I interjected. "My friend says you speak English very well."

"I was just trying to do my assignment," Jamie said to me as the waitress walked into the kitchen. "You know, getting to know the people. It's my journalistic curiosity at work, that's all. Heck, it's my job."

We later learned that this young waitress, who was actually forty-nine, had come to Israel as a child with her parents and nine siblings in Operation Magic Carpet, the airlift that brought the Jews of Yemen to Israel. They were a devout group of Jews who had never before seen an airplane, and they were coming to Israel "on wings of eagles," as the Bible says. They, along with Jews from other Arab lands like Iraq, Tunisia, and Morocco are referred to as *Sephardim*, a Hebrew word originally referring to Jews from Spain and Portugal, but later applied to Jews from Arab lands, too. For years they were discriminated against in Israeli society—in education, housing, welfare, job opportunities—because they came from technologically backward societies or because of the dark color of their skin. Marriage between them and others was rare. For whatever the reason, the European *Ashkenazim,* who founded and led the country in the formative years, often excluded the Sephardim from positions of power and advancement.

While much progress has been made in the condition of Sephardim in recent years, the problem of their exclusion from Israeli public leadership still reverberates in society.

"Watch out for those," warned our waitress, pointing to green peppers on our plate. "They are very hot."

Seeking to impress her with his machismo, Jamie took a whole pepper and popped it in his mouth. "I've traveled the world over. It can't be hotter than Mexican jalapeños." He learned better. His face turned fiery red, and perspiration appeared on his brow.

I then showed Jamie how to eat this exotic Yemenite food. "We dip the special Yemenite pita bread called *mellawach* in hummus," I explained, "break off some *shaweeya*, which is another kind of pita bread, and dip it in *techina* sauce."

"Delicious," he said the instant it touched his palate.

"And how meaningful it is to break bread together with you."

"Makes me want to become Yemenite," added Jamie. "That and the pretty waitress. Oh, don't fret, Rabbi. I won't ask for her phone number."

יְהֹוָה

We finished lunch and walked through the crowded streets of Jerusalem. As we passed a storefront synagogue, I turned to Jamie. "I need to *daven mincha*, recite my after-noon prayers. There's a *minyan* starting here in five min-utes. Remember what a *minyan* is?"

"Yes, a harem, I mean quorum," he said jokingly, "of ten men needed for a prayer service. Right?"

"Correct," I said. "Mincha services last about ten min-utes. Come on in with me."

Jamie put on his yarmulke and entered the synagogue with me. The service lasted longer than I anticipated since the rabbi was giving a *dvar Torah,* brief *Torah* message. Ideally, every Jewish prayer experience should also have a learning component to it. A *pushke* or charity box was passed around, since giving *tzedakah* or charity is another component of prayer.

יְהֹוָה

"What shall I bring back for my brother?" Jamie asked after services as we passed dozens of small gift shops in the mall. "And for my secretary?"

"The ultimate tourist concern," I responded. "You can always bring back Israeli sunflower seeds."

Israelis love to eat sunflower seeds. People walk through the streets, especially on the Sabbath when smoking is prohibited, eating sunflower seeds and spitting the shells on the ground. Israel is probably the only country in the world with this sign in movie theaters: IT IS PROHIBITED TO SMOKE OR TO CRACK SUNFLOWER SEEDS HERE.

We entered a store where Jamie selected a set of praying hands carved out of olive wood.

"How much is this?" he asked in English.

"Twenty-eight dollars," said the man behind the counter, instantly recognizing that he was dealing with a naive American.

"Okay, I'll take it," said Jamie.

"No, he won't," I said in my best Hebrew. "That's way overpriced."

"Did I say *dollars*?" said the owner quickly. "I meant *shekels*."

"Okay," I said, "that's fair."

Taking advantage of tourists is common everywhere in the world. But in the Middle East, one isn't expected to pay the amount first quoted, especially in the marketplace. One is expected to haggle and even walk out of the shop if a deal isn't cut with the storekeeper.

"You should always counteroffer by dropping the asking price by at least half," I explained to Jamie, "provided, of course, you are really prepared to purchase the item for that amount. Merchants can get terribly angry if they agree to a counteroffer and you do not buy it."

We decided to make a quick visit to the Knesset, the Israeli parliament. In front of the building is a large menorah, national symbol of the State of Israel, representing knowledge, spirit, and religious freedom. The ancient menorah that was in the temple and upon which this model was based was taken into exile by the Romans in 70 C.E. A sketch of it can still be seen today on the base of the Arc de Triomphe in Paris. Jews believe that for two thousand years the light of the menorah remained in exile. But with the reestablishment of the State of Israel, the menorah and all it represents was restored to its homeland. The role of Israel, today more than ever before, is to be a "light unto the nations," to remind the world—and the Jews themselves—of the words of Zerubabel, "Not by might, nor by power, but by My spirit—said the LORD of Hosts."

We passed through the heavy security and entered the main building, a much humbler, less ostentatious edifice than the U.S. Capitol. Most Knesset members are low key, dressing informally with no tie or jacket. Beautiful Chagall windows adorned the walls and refracted the rays of sunlight, adding beauty and brightness to the deliberations inside.

A session at the Knesset is dramatically different from that of the U.S. Senate, for example, and marked by a distinct lack of decorum and courtesy. In American politics, a heated debate might lead a senator to boldly stand up from his chair and declare, "Mr. Speaker, I disagree strongly with the gentleman from Virginia." In contrast with American niceties and formalities, a Knesset minister might actually scream at another—even at the Prime Minister—and call him derogatory names.

Jamie, a calm and cool WASP, was quite taken by this Israeli phenomenon, and uncertain whether to attribute it to a uniquely Jewish or generically Middle East characteristic. Whatever its root, there was something intriguing and beguiling for him about the pathos exhibited, all airs and pretenses stripped away and people desperately searching for truth, justice, and physical security.

"You know what this reminds me of?" he said as we walked out of the main building. "The yeshiva we visited the other day where I saw that same all-out energy directed at understanding God's word. I must admit, I tend to see Jesus through my Protestant- tainted eyes, as a quiet, well-mannered, docile man with blond hair and soft features. But now I realize that perhaps he was not at all like that. Jesus was a Jew, the progeny of Abraham who had the audacity to actually argue with God, a descendent of Jacob who fought with the angel and stubbornly would not let him leave till he blessed him. I'll bet if Jesus were alive today, he'd be screaming at the top of his lungs in there about the injustices in society."

I laughed. "You mean to tell me that after four days in Israel you've come to realize that Jesus was not a WASP but a Jew? You've come a long way, baby!"

Just when Jamie thought it safe to reclaim the Jewishness of Jesus, we heard church bells ringing. "Ah yes," sighed Jamie. "Christians have a claim to Jerusalem too!"

"And to this land," I added. "The Crusaders never acknowledged this as Jewish land, and neither did the Muslims. The church bells bespeak the Christian claim. But five times a day you can hear the chanting of the Arab Muziim calling Muslims to prayer throughout the city, and reminding Jews of the ancient—and present—Moslem claims to this sacred land. While Jews' love for Israel and attachment to her trumps that of every other group, no single faith community has exclusive claims to this land, and that is the core of the political conflict today."

When we returned to our hotel late at night, I finally had the chance to read my copy of the *Jerusalem Post*. On the front page was the story of how, after a nine-year separation, an Ethiopian Jewish child was finally airlifted to Israel where she joined her family. The young girl had apparently gotten lost escaping Ethiopia in 1981 during her long trek to Sudan from where she and others were to be airlifted to Israel. This little girl became separated from the rest of her family who, after searching for days, finally gave up on finding her alive and moved on with their escape. With the help of the Israeli authorities, however, the search for her continued. Finally, nine years later, the girl was found and airlifted to Israel.

What an incredible, heartwarming story to read, of the reunification of a tormented Jewish family, and the moral foundations of the State of Israel that led it to go to such extreme lengths to help even one imperiled Jew find safety in Israel.

The simple act of reading the daily newspaper is a reminder that in Israel one is not just a distant bystander watching events take place, but an active participant and partner with God in the unfolding of history and dramatic fulfillment of biblical prophecy. My evening prayers were especially meaningful to me that night, inspired as they were by the day's packed events and by the daily newspaper.

CHAPTER TWELVE

OUR DRIVE AROUND THE OLD CITY WALLS

We stepped out of the hotel, refreshed from a good night's sleep, ready to begin a new day in Jerusalem.

"I'm charley-horsed from all the walking we're doing," complained Jamie. "Let's rent a car for the day and drive around Jerusalem."

We began with a tour of the Old City or eastern portion, referred to by many Western journalists as Arab East Jerusalem. The fact that King David established it as Israel's capital long before Islam even arose, and that there has been an uninterrupted Jewish presence there for three thousand years, goes totally unnoticed by the Arab population.

We drove around the majestic walls, built by the Turkish Sultan in the 1500s, that surround the old city. Every few hundred meters we passed a large gate providing entry into the city. The names of these gates reflect the claims put forth by different groups asserting their unique rights in this city. We passed the Damascus Gate, so known because it faces Syria; Herod's Gate, which leads to the Garden Tomb; and the gate known as Stephen's Gate by Christians, Lions' Gate by Jews, and Mary's Gate by Arabs. Christians refer to it that way because, according to their tradition, Stephen, the first Christian martyr, was taken out of these Jerusalem gates and stoned. Jews refer to it as the Lions' Gate because of the images of lions carved on it. According to ancient legend, the Sultan who built the wall dreamed that lions would devour him if he did not beautify Jerusalem. When he awakened, he ordered that large walls be built to protect and beautify the city. The Lions' Gate was also the one through which the Israeli paratroopers entered when the Old City was recaptured in 1967. Arabs refer to it as Mary's Gate because of their tradition that it marks the birthplace of Mary, mother of Jesus.

"I was wondering about something," said Jamie out of the blue. "I recently rented the video of Spielberg's film *Raiders of the Lost Ark*. Whatever really happened to the Tabernacle and the Ark when the Temple was destroyed?"

"We just don't know," I said. Some believe it was taken to Ethiopia; others believe it remained in Jerusalem and was buried somewhere in the Old City. The Talmud proffers that it may be buried under the Temple Mount, though we are prohibited from searching there until the messiah comes since we are impure and need to wait for him to sprinkle the ashes of the red heifer on us."

"Do you really believe in that?" Jamie asked. "In the coming of Messiah? And not believe that Jesus was the one sent by God the Father to bring salvation to mankind?"

I hesitated for a moment to answer. Was Jamie trying to proselytize me? Or was he just coming to grips with his Christian faith and Baptist upbringing? I gave him the benefit of the doubt.

"Yes," I said finally. "I really do believe in the coming of *mashiach* and redemption of mankind. I just don't believe they are to be found in Jesus."

"And if," asked Jamie, "when he comes, he'll have holes in his hands and feet from the nails of the crucifix?"

"If that happens," I said meekly, "I'll say two Hail Marys and publicly admit I was wrong."

"Fair enough," said Jamie, smiling.

We both felt we won.

"What will the third temple look like?" asked Jamie.

"There are a number of museums in Jerusalem with models of both of the two ancient temples, as well as the future one which the messiah will build."

"One quick question," said Jamie hastily, "a parting shot, if you will. Do you think that when the Messiah comes it will be his first or second coming?" The smirk on his face told me he knew he was pushing this issue to the limit.

"I'll tell you what, Jamie. Why don't we both adopt a wait-and-see attitude?"

"Fair enough," he said. And, again, we both felt we had come out winners.

יְהֹוָה

We passed Nablus Gate and saw a group of Arabs waiting patiently in a long, straight line.

"An unemployment line?" Jamie asked.

"No," I answered. "They're waiting for the Ministry of Interior to open so they can get a visa to travel out of the country. And you see those people over there, across the street? They're helping others who don't know how to read or write to type out the necessary forms."

We went around a bend and saw three or four dark-skinned Israeli border police blocking off traffic.

"They're Sephardim, right?" said Jamie proudly, remembering our Yemenite waitress from the restaurant.

"Actually, they're Druse," I said, "a Muslim sect, whose members serve in the Israel army and are loyal to the State of Israel. Yesterday, five cars were firebombed here in a terrorist incident."

While lightning isn't supposed to strike twice in the same place, we prudently decided to park the car a few blocks away. We walked around a bit near the Damascus Gate, gazing at the exotic people, bargaining with the shopkeepers, and buying *chatchkees* or knickknacks along the way. We returned to our car, thankfully still in one piece.

We drove up a narrow, one-lane dirt road leading to the top of Mount Olives and almost collided with a car coming down.

"What are we going to do now?" asked Jamie.

"We'll have to back down to the bottom of the hill and let him go first," I said. "The one going down has the right of way."

The roads had been made for donkeys and buggies, not cars and buses. Eventually we reached the top of the mountain. Holding on to my yarmulke, which was almost blown away by the strong wind, I gazed at the incredible panorama of Jerusalem before us.

"See over there," I said, pointing to the southeast corner of the Old City. "That is regarded by Christians as the most important part of the ancient temple area. According to Christian belief, it was there that, after fasting and wandering in the desert for forty days and nights and being tempted by Satan to eat after he was baptized by John, Jesus sat and began his ministry."

Jamie was dumbstruck. "Right over there?" he said, pointing. "That's amazing! I remember reading about that in Sunday school. That's actually the place where Jesus began his ministry? Amazing! Just awesome."

"Yep," I said. "But nothing in Israel is simple. There's another Christian tradition that insists that Jesus sat on the south*west* corner of the city. The source for this view is an inscription on a rock found in that area stating that site was the place of trumpets that were blown to announce the Jewish New Year and Day of Atonement. Many believe that the blowing of the trumpets referred not to the holy days, but to the ushering in of the messiah, presumed to be Jesus by whoever wrote that inscription."

"Cool," said Jamie taking it all in. "Really cool."

The magnificent view of the city from the Mount of Olives is one of the most inspirational in all of Israel, the one most frequently displayed on postcards and television shows. We walked past the site that Judas purchased with the money given to him as a bribe. It is referred to as "the field of money," which is a double entendre. For in Hebrew, *damin*, the word for *money*, also means "blood." It was, in other words, "blood money."

We passed the Church of All Nations, sometimes called the Church of Agony. Built in 1921 by a consortium of thirteen Catholic groups, it marks the place where Jesus sat on the rock, wept, and felt forsaken in what is known as "the night of agony." This is also where Judas betrayed Jesus with a kiss.

"Look at all the incredible olive trees, Jamie," I said, pointing directly in front of us. "Did you know that some of the oldest olive trees in the Middle East are right here, many as old as twenty-eight hundred years and still bearing fruit today?"

"Awesome." Jamie sighed. "Really cool."

"See over there," I said, pointing to the gate in front of the Mosque of Omar on the Temple Mount. "That's called the Golden or Eastern Gate."

"Because of the gold dome of the mosque," Jamie said, "and the fact that it's on the eastern part of the city, right?"

"Very good, Jamie. You're getting the hang of it. But you didn't notice something—it's the only gate that is closed."

"You're right, I didn't notice that."

"It was sealed centuries ago, and a cemetery was placed immediately in front of it."

"I can see the cemetery from here," said Jamie.

"According to ancient biblical tradition," I continued, "when the messiah comes, he will rest his feet on the Mount of Olives and cross through that gate to the Temple Mount to bring salvation to the world. According to an ancient legend, the Arabs sealed the gate and placed a cemetery in front of it. This was to prevent the messiah, who is a descendent of David and from the priestly clan, from crossing there since a priest must be safeguarded from impurity and may not walk through a cemetery."

"Really?" asked Jamie.

"Just a legend," I admit. "But who knows?"

"Talking about cemeteries, what is this huge cemetery we're standing on?" asked Jamie, pointing to the foot of the mountain all the way up to the top where we were standing.

"It is an ancient Jewish cemetery," I explained, "probably the oldest functioning cemetery in the world, dating back to the time of King David."

"King David?" asked Jamie in amazement.

"Yes, already three thousand years ago, Jews' bodies were brought here outside the city walls for burial. In the Jewish tradition, it is considered a great privilege to be buried on the Mount of Olives since it is so close to the temple area and when the messiah comes the resurrection of the dead will begin here. In fact, my great grandfather, after whom I am named, and many of my relatives are buried here. The late Prime Minister Begin is also buried here, as are other prominent Israeli Jews.

"Tragically, Jamie, when this area, along with the entire Old City, was captured by Jordan in 1948, most of the tombstones were toppled, desecrated, and ruined. Some of the stones were even used as backs for latrines. And that hotel over there was built on top of the cemetery. After the

Israeli capture of the area in 1967, the tombstones were restored. I remember my father and his brothers and sisters paying to restore my great grandfather's tombstone."

We drove on to a convent built on the site where Jesus taught the apostles the Lord's Prayer.

"It was here that Jesus predicted the destruction of Jerusalem," I explained.

"Yeah," added Jamie, "and where he declared that not even one stone would remain resting on top of another."

"Very good," I said. "You must have had a good Sunday school teacher. But did you know that this actually happened? According to tradition, when the Second Temple was destroyed, the fire melted the gold of the altar and the gold ran down and hardened on top of the rocks below. Seeing that, the Roman soldiers chiseled out the gold by removing all the stones, fulfilling Jesus' prediction that no stone would remain on top of another."

"Awesome. Just awesome. You must have had a great Sunday school teacher too!" said Jamie smiling.

יהוה

We visited the Chapel of Ascension where, according to tradition, Jesus ascended to heaven on the thirtieth day after his resurrection from the dead. Originally a church from the Byzantine period, it was later taken over by Moslems and turned into a mosque.

"You see, Jamie," I explained, "here in Jerusalem, each ruling power not only built on top of prior generations, but usurped them."

"Just like the Jordanians did in this century when they built a hotel on the Jewish cemetery on the Mount of Olives," he added.

"That's right. I guess the moral challenge the Israelis face today is how to build a new civilization in the place of older ones, but not at their expense, and how to revitalize Jewish life here, while protecting the religious and civil rights of others. Now that, to use your lingo, is an awesome challenge."

יְהוָֹה

We came to a church overlooking Mount Zion where, according to Christian tradition, God appeared to Jesus in the Upper Room as the Holy Spirit. I explained to Jamie that Christians come here to celebrate the Day of Ascension thirty days after Easter.

An Arab approached us, offering a good exchange rate for our dollars. Jamie and I looked at one another and, with a knowing smile, together said, "Moneychangers." Interesting how we both were immediately reminded of the New Testament references to the corrupt moneychangers in the Temple who had stood just a few yards away from where we were standing. Two thousand years later, little has changed; tourists flocking to Jerusalem need to exchange their money and, no doubt, bargain for a good rate.

יְהוָֹה

We drove back to the Mount of Olives and visited a church called the Fada Nostra, meaning "our father in heaven."

"I remember that," shouted Jamie. "That's where the disciples asked Jesus to teach them to pray."

"Correct," I said approvingly.

"According to tradition, it was here that Jesus not only taught his disciples to pray, but also where he predicted the coming destruction of the Temple," Jamie says.

We walked down to the grotto upon which the church marking this site was built. I explained to Jamie how this church was also one of the six built by Helena, mother of Constantine, though not the original. The only church that Helena built and that still stands in its original form is the Church of the Nativity; some sections of Santa Caterina also are standing. The Moslems tore down all the others during Byzantine times.

"Another instance of culture usurping culture," said Jamie, "as if we haven't seen enough."

We gazed at the walls of the church. On them was written the Lord's Prayer in different languages, including French, Fijian, Hebrew, and Aramaic.

"It's amazing," I pointed out, "how this beautiful prayer and church have become embraced by people of so many different cultures and even faiths. It has really become a universal prayer, more than almost any other."

A group of Italian tourists was standing in a circle holding hands, eyes closed softly, reciting the Lord's Prayer. They were wearing buttons on their lapels that featured a large cross in the middle with four smaller ones representing five continents and five crusades on the sides.

It was a very moving scene. We could feel the power of holiness gripping the group and exuding from this place. Add to that a magnificent echo. It was a profound, mystical experience that would touch even the most cynical atheist. Jamie joined them in reciting the prayer.

"It's incredible to realize I am chanting the Lord's Prayer in the actual place where Jesus taught his disciples to pray. Truly overwhelming. Thank you for bringing me here, Yechiel," he said, somehow not butchering my name.

"I know what you're thinking. I said your name pretty well, huh? Actually, I've been practicing each night in my room, but I've been afraid to say it to you.

"Anyhow," he continued, tears welling in his eyes, "I'm so appreciative that I'm here. You see, of everything I learned and experienced in church as a child, it was the Lord's Prayer—Give us this day our daily bread and forgive us our trespasses, as we forgive those who trespass against us—that has always stayed with me. It's a simple plea to God for life, and in a strange way has always spoken to me more than any other prayer."

יהוה

We visited the sixth-century church of Dominas Plavit, the lord who cried, marking the site where Jesus shed tears over the future suffering and destruction of the city of Jerusalem. The Italian pastor was reading the portions of the New Testament relating to this site.

As we left the church, we overheard an Israeli guide boasting to his tour group about how fluent he is in Arabic and how well he gets along with Arabs. "They know I am more powerful, and I don't have to show it," he said. "The less you show your power, the more it is left to their imagination. They know that I am strong. That is the main thing."

I was embarrassed by this Israeli's arrogant bravado, especially in contrast to the Italian pastor's soft humility. But not as embarrassed as I was when Jamie began singing, loud enough for everyone to hear the song, "Macho, macho man, I've got to be a macho man." In light of my recent vow not to judge others, my initial revulsion with the tour guide's condescending comments was mitigated. After all, who was I, living comfortably as I do in Chicago, to pass judgment on his character and teach him the "proper" relationship Israelis should have with Arabs? Here in Israel, the relationship between Arabs and Jews is, indeed, shaped by the question of who has and who does not have, power. And, of course, those who have it wield it.

יְהוָה

We walked down the mountain toward the Garden of Gethsemane, believed to be the site of Jesus' "night of agony" before he was betrayed. On the way, we passed the Valley of Johoshaphat where, according to the prophecy of Zachariah, the final judgment will take place. It lies in the upper part of the Kidron Valley, between the Mount of Olives and the Golden Gate. There is a monument for Saint Stephen who, according to tradition, was stoned at this place.

"The word *Gethsemane* actually comes from the Hebrew term *gat shemen*, olive press," I explained. Looking around, it was not hard to understand why, nor why the entire mountain is called Mount of Olives.

"Now I understand!" exclaimed Jamie, all excited.

"Understand what?"

"Now I understand why Paul, in Romans nine through eleven, used the metaphor of the Gentiles being grafted onto the rich *olive tree* of Israel. With all the olive trees around Jerusalem, it was a natural image for Paul to draw upon."

"Come to Israel," I responded, somewhat mockingly. "See the Bible come alive and understand it for the first time."

All of Jamie's childhood memories and lessons from Sunday school come to the fore as a flood of Bible teachings rolled off his tongue.

"According to the New Testament, after leaving Lazarus's home in Bethany and finding himself unwelcome in Jerusalem in the last days of his life, Jesus was forced to stay outside the city walls here in a cave, in the grotto of Gethsemane. On Thursday night."

"Which was probably Passover," I interjected.

"On Thursday night of Passover," Jamie continued, "Jesus went to the Upper Room for the Last Supper, and later returned to Gethsemane. That evening, he sat alone on a rock near here, and he later returned to the grotto of Gethsemane with his disciples, Peter, James, and John. It was then that Judas came with a policeman of Caiaphas, the High Priest, and betrayed Jesus with a kiss." Jamie smiled proudly as he remembered these details, realizing how deeply his earlier years in church had affected him.

"Just goes to show you," I said. "You can take the journalist out of Christianity, but you can't take the Christianity out of the journalist."

Unfortunately, even religious sites like Gethsemane often become commercialized, probably because of the constant need for funds to maintain them. To enter the Garden we paid a fee, which was upsetting to Jamie. But not as upsetting as the Arab children and adults who accosted us asking for money or selling souvenir trinkets almost every step we took. Throngs of Christian tourists come here to this small confined space, making it difficult to park or even get around. The Arab peddlers often frighten Americans, who are unaccustomed to the in-your-face aggressiveness of the people here.

"Two pieces of advice I have for you, Jamie. First, put your wallet in your front pocket. Second, try not to let all this commotion annoy or distract you from the sacredness of this site and your spiritual pilgrimage."

"I receive both pieces of advice," he said gratefully, making sure his wallet was secure.

Anticipating my next question, he said, "Oh, *receiving* is Christianese for accepting in his spirit. See, I can teach you a thing or two."

We walked a hundred yards, found a decent rest room— no small achievement—paid the Arab guard, and entered. As we walked out, Jamie said, "The thought that I relieved myself on such holy ground seems almost sacrilegious."

Jamie, it seemed, was not only recovering his Christian faith, he was developing a serious case of Jerusalem fever, a not uncommon malady afflicting visitors, and often leading them to become mystics. Jamie's editor would never forgive me. In Israel the spiritual and the carnal, the ancient and the contemporary, mesh as one. Yes, even Abraham, Isaac, Jacob, and Jesus relieved themselves. A few yards from the Garden is the Church of All Nations, sometimes referred to as the Church of Agony. It faces the Golden Gate, which leads directly to where the Holy of Holies was in the ancient Temple.

"In other words," explained Jamie, now on a teaching roll, "the rock on which Jesus sat in the Garden of Gethsemane was in a straight line with the Holy of Holies."

"Correct," I said, adding, "and if you go in the opposite direction, you come to the Chapel of Ascension on the Mount of Olives where the ashes of the red heifer were burned."

Tourists walked up and kissed the rock, much like I reverentially kissed the stones of the *Kotel* just a few days earlier.

"I guess we're not that far apart after all," Jamie said. "We both imbue stone with holiness."

יהוה

It was Monday, which meant that the Wall was crowded with Jewish worshipers. Ever since the time of the prophet Ezra, the *Torah* is read publicly in the morning services on Mondays and Thursdays. As a result, bar mitzvahs are often celebrated on those days. The thirteen-year-old boy reads from the *Torah* scroll as his first public ritual act as a Jewish adult. Family members and friends come to the Wall from all over the world to celebrate the occasion. That day, there were fourteen different bar mitzvah celebrations. As we entered the spacious promenade in front of the Wall, we passed a group of Hassidim dressed in long black coats and hats, a monk from Italy, and two girls with knapsacks, cutoff jeans, and tank tops. Different as they are, they're all going to pray at the same holy place, and to the same holy God.

"What does that mean?" Jamie asked, pointing to a Hebrew sign on top of a car.

"Oh, you see those all over Israel. It says, 'Prepare yourselves for the coming of messiah.' It's part of an ad campaign sponsored by the Lubavitch Hassidim."

"Like the signs in America saying, 'Jesus saves,'" added Jamie.

"Yeah, I guess so. Actually, it's more like John the Baptist's campaign from two thousand years ago to prepare the way for the coming of the Messiah. This is simply the contemporary Jewish version."

יהוה

Jerusalem is a true melting pot for all sorts of religious groups—Jews, Moslems, and Christians of all stripes—each claiming exclusive possession of truth. There are Armenians, Greek Orthodox, Catholics, and dozens of Protestant groups. The model for dealing with such religious diversity was adopted long ago from the Roman city planners who divided neighborhoods into four quadrants, with two intersecting streets running through the length and width of the area. The one going from north to south was called the Cardo; that going from east to west was called the Decomonos. For generations, the city of Jerusalem has been similarly divided into Armenian, Jewish, Christian, and Moslem Quarters.

We entered the newly rebuilt Jewish quarter where my father and grandparents were born. The entire area was virtually destroyed after 1948 when it came under Jordanian control. Smack in the middle of the Jewish quarter, and higher than all the other buildings, is a mosque. And in the adjacent Christian quarter is a church with a cross that is higher than all the other edifices surrounding it. I explained to Jamie how, for centuries, Jews were not allowed to build edifices as large as Moslem ones, even in their own quarter.

"That's interesting," said Jamie. "But frankly what impresses me most is the fact that now, even though the Moslem quarter is under Jewish control, there is no similar effort to pay them back. You can take pride in the way you Jews treat the holy sites of other faith communities under your control."

"Don't forget to put that in your articles," I said, reminding him of my concern that he write favorably and truthfully about Israel's cause. I was relieved and assured he'd do just that.

There is a saying in the Middle East that one cannot create the new and charming without preserving the old and honorable. This maxim served as the guiding principle for Israeli architects who rebuilt the new Jewish quarter on top of the remains of the old, trying to stay true to the old forms of masonry and integrating them into the new.

"Some of the homes here have rocks painted blue at their base," said Jamie.

"Astute observation," I said. "These are older homes, pre-1948, that were painted blue to keep away the *ayin horah,* the evil eye."

"But why blue?" Jamie asks.

"Blue was the color of the *tzizit,* the fringes on the prayer shawl, that remind us of heaven, which is also blue and which, in turn, reminds us of God."

"It's also the color of the Israeli flag," noted Jamie.

It's easy to lose sight of the fact that while for us a walk through the Jewish Quarter is a tour of ancient Jewish history, for the Jews living here, it is life as normal. Kids playing football, women walking with baby strollers, men rushing to work, a group of Israeli schoolchildren touring the area with their teacher, a young woman in civilian clothes carrying an Uzi—all are evident. Because of the terrorist attacks against schoolchildren, it is a law in Israel that an armed adult must accompany every school group.

"Can you imagine if every time school kids went out on a picnic back home they had to have an armed guard accompanying them? I don't know how Israelis live like that. Or what it does to the children's psyche and sense of security and well-being," Jamie said.

A huge construction crane was building something there, dwarfing everything in sight. And in front of one of the restaurants was a pool table, just a few feet from an ancient archeological dig. The old and the new are intertwined here, the modern and the ancient. Life goes on.

We noticed an entourage of security and diplomatic cars arriving at the Kotel. The new president of Ethiopia, who was visiting Israel that week, wanted to pray at the Wall. Jews take pride in their abhorrence of racism. How ironic that the world community, through a landslide vote in the United Nations, equated Zionism with racism. In fact, Israel is the only country in history to travel thousands of miles away from its shores to bring black people from Africa to freedom, not slavery. The entire black Jewish community of Ethiopia, descendants of the tribe of Dan and/or the Queen of Sheba and Solomon, today live in Israel.

Continuing our walk through the Jewish quarter, we saw a group of Christian Zionists from Germany. On the bags were emblems with the Star of David and the word *Yeshua*, Hebrew for "Jesus," written on it.

"Jews must appreciate such philo-Semitic gestures," said Jamie, "insofar as they reflect their return to their Jewish roots."

"Actually," I replied, "most Jews are offended by them and see them as disingenuous attempts to camouflage their true missionary intentions with presumably acceptable Jewish language and symbols."

"Sounds to me like some dialogue on this matter would be useful," said Jamie.

We toured the Burnt House—the destroyed basement of a wealthy first-century aristocratic Jewish family that made the spices for the temple worship.

"It's incredible," exclaimed Jamie. "You can still see the two-thousand-year-old charred wood panels preserved from the original edifice."

"And look over there, under the protective glass," I pointed out. "That's the actual hand of a woman who was grasping for a spear as the Romans were attacking. The panels and hand were able to survive intact because they were buried under the destroyed house, which fell into the basement.

We passed a small store where an elderly Jewish man with a long white beard was sitting and reciting the Psalms, quietly alone, waiting for customers.

"I wish I had a camera," said Jamie. "That is a beautiful scene."

We came to the Churva, the main synagogue in the Jewish quarter from approximately 1850 to 1948, now lying in ruins. It became known by this name since it was built on top of the Ramban Synagogue, which dated back to the Byzantine Period, sixth century, and was destroyed by Jordan in 1948, save for its famous arch that remained relatively intact. The Churva Synagogue was rebuilt and again used for prayers. Like the burning bush, the fire of Judaism and bonds Jews feel for this land will never be extinguished.

Fire may singe the Jewish people, but the fire will not consume them.

We came across an army unit also touring the Jewish Quarter. Such tours are part of the regular army training program, strategically familiarizing the soldiers with the land and deepening their attachment to it so they know what values they are fighting for.

Jamie noticed one of the soldiers wearing an emblem with a snake on it.

"Why the snake?" he asked.

"That means he is part of a medical unit," I answered. "The snake is the most ancient Jewish symbol for healing. It stems from the biblical story in which Moses raised his hands in the battle against Amalek. When he did so, the people of Israel were victorious. When he lowered them, they suffered losses. Similarly, when the Israelites were attacked by poisonous snakes, Moses, standing on the mountaintop, raised his staff and the people who looked up to it were saved."

"I never understood that," said Jamie. "Why would looking up save them from snakebites?"

"There is a beautiful lesson in the story," I explained. "The Talmud states that it was not Moses' raised hands or the snake on a stick that actually saved the people of Israel. Rather, when they looked up to Moses on top of the mountain, they were actually turning to God and giving their heart to their father in heaven. That is the reason they were saved."

"That's nice," said Jamie. "I'm not sure that's what was meant by the text, but it's a nice interpretation."

I was again struck by the fact that here I was, an Orthodox rabbi, engaging in biblical hermeneutics and exegesis with a Baptist journalist.

"Cool," said Jamie.

"Indeed," I said.

יְהוָה

We continued our tour and came to the remnants of a large wall referred to in Isaiah 22:10-11 and built by Hezekiah around 271 B.C.E. to protect the Siloah Pool and the Jews living inside and outside Jerusalem, the City of David. The source of the city's water in biblical times was the Gichon Springs at the foot of the Mountain of David outside the city. Concerned that Jerusalem might be surrounded during the war, Hezekiah built a tunnel to carry the spring water into the City of David and the Siloah Pool, and he built a fortified wall to defend the area. It is the remnants of that ancient wall that Nehemiah, who lived a hundred years later described in chapters 3 and 12. Walking along, Jamie and I now saw it. People walk through the tunnel, too, though we didn't have the time to do so on this trip.

"It's always good to leave something for next time," I said.

"So you think we'll be back here again, huh?" Jamie asked.

"I'm sure of it," I said, "if not together then separately."

We walked through the narrow alleyways of the Jewish quarter.

"It must be easy to get lost here if you don't know your way around," said Jamie.

We made our way to the Christian side and came to the Via Dolorosa, part of the Stations of the Cross, the fourteen places where Jesus suffered in the process of his crucifixion. Every Friday, Catholics reenact Jesus' walk of the Stations of the Cross. We came to the first station where Jesus' trial took place, and then moved to the second where Jesus took up the cross.

"Can you feel his pain?" Jamie asked with a degree of earnestness I had not seen from him before. "Jesus died for you and me," he continued, "for the whole world. He took upon himself this incredible pain and suffering so that man would have salvation from sin. Can't you believe in that?"

Jamie was treading very close to the no-proselytizing line we had implicitly established. His theological narrowness and exclusivity might have offended other Jews, who believe that there is only one way to truth. I knew better and saw it for what it really was—Jamie was coming to grips with his faith. Let him be proud of it, I thought, and shout it from the rooftops for all to hear... and for all to reject if they so chose. Jamie was not being intolerant by declaring his faith and sharing it with me. He was coming alive. And rather than shutting him up, I wanted to encourage him. For I genuinely believe if Christians were better Christians and Jews better Jews, we'd have a much better world and a much more decent society.

"No," I said gently, "I don't believe that. Actually, most Jews regard such views as so foreign and antithetical to their faith and reason they wonder how intelligent people can believe it."

I don't think Jamie heard a word I said. He was entering a spiritual zone I had not seen him enter before.

"Don't you see?" he said, suddenly sobbing. "He died for me, sinner that I am." With that, Jamie broke down and cried uncontrollably, "O Jesus, sweet Jesus. I'm sorry for my sins. O Jesus, thank you for saving me. O Jesus..."

I stood in awe and silence as I watched his born again transformation and what God was doing to his heart. Jamie could not speak. He just sat down on the ground, clasped his head in his hands, and wept.

"O Jesus," he finally said between sobs, "I accept you as my personal Lord and Savior. I receive you as my Lord, my Christ, my friend.

"Fill me, father, with your Holy Spirit, that I may serve you faithfully all the days of my life. You are my lord, and in the name of Jesus, I pray. Amen. Thank you, father, thank you, father, thank you..."

Jamie looked at me tearfully, almost oblivious to my presence yet eager to hear my reaction. Frankly, I didn't know what to say. I had never witnessed anything quite like that before, except on those television evangelist shows of which I am rather skeptical, even cynical. A beautiful peace seemed to come over Jamie, as if the burden of life's struggles was lifted from him. I envied him that peace.

"My tears were tears of joy," he said, before I could comment, with a big smile crossing his face, eyes twinkling in delight. "Praise God, I am saved. Amazing grace."

"*Kol hakavod*," I said. "*Kol hakavod.*"

"What does that mean?" asked Jamie with a new softness I found endearing.

"Well, literally, Jamie, it means 'with all respect.' It's a popular Israeli phrase, the highest compliment you can give someone. It means, Good for you, you have my respect for what you did."

"Is that the way you feel about the scene you just witnessed? I didn't mean to make you uncomfortable, but I just couldn't help it. I was so overcome by God's spirit and was gripped by the realization that Jesus is the truth."

"He's *your* truth, Jamie," I interjected, "and I'm happy for you."

"Okay," said Jamie, "now is not the time to debate that. But thank you for bringing me here and being patient and understanding with me." Pausing a second, he continued with a smirk. "But how do I tell people it was an Orthodox rabbi who brought me to become a born-again Christian?"

"You mean Jesus, your lord?" I said wryly.

"No, you."

"How do *you* tell your friends?" I asked, "how do *I* tell mine?"

יְהוָה

We sat for a few more moments before continuing our walk in the Christian Quarter. We passed a monument in memory of a young Jewish rabbinical student who was killed there two years ago. In Israel, time and faith are inextricably intertwined—Christian, Moslem, and Jewish. We walked a few more yards and come to the third station, where Jesus fell with the cross. We proceeded another few yards to the fourth station where he met his mother, and a few more steps to the fifth where Simon helped Jesus carry the heavy cross. The Via Dolorosa culminates at the Church of the Holy Sepulchre, which contains the last five stations of the cross. It is here, say Catholics, that Jesus was crucified on a rock shaped like a skull, or *golgotha* in Hebrew. Protestants, who for centuries were barred from this Catholic church, discredit the authenticity of the site and believe that Jesus was crucified in a different place called the Garden Tomb.

We stopped to buy a sweet Turkish candy from one of the Arab shops lining the narrow cobblestone streets, whiffed the distinctive aroma of the Arab shuk, and marveled at its exotic character. Shops sold carvings made of olive wood, camera equipment, shoes, souvenirs, T-shirts, candy, and more. Arabic music playing in the shops could be heard throughout the streets.

"I'll never understand," said Jamie, "how all the different people, cultures, and religious groups—each with their own distinctive needs, historical claims, and mores—are able to get along together. Boy, I could never be the mayor here. Talk about an impossible job."

"It's a challenge. For example, the Church of the Holy Sepulcher has to accommodate five different denominations of Catholic and Orthodox Christians by designating specific times daily when each group controls the site." We walked into the Church of the Holy Sepulcher.

"A far cry from my Protestant Baptist church," said Jamie, gazing at the elaborate ornaments, candles, and incense filling the hall. "We Protestants have a hard time dealing with this stuff," he continued. "It's so carnal and gaudy and ritualistic; I really feel that it detracts from the primary function of the church, which is to create an atmosphere for receiving the Holy Spirit and being inspired by God's presence."

"That's fine," I responded patiently, "but don't forget about tolerance and respect for non-Protestant believers."

יהוה

Many scholars believe that Jesus was hung on the cross on Friday morning at around nine A.M. and declared dead at around three in the afternoon. But since Jesus was a Jew, according to the *Torah*, he needed to be buried by sundown on that same day. That is why Saint Joseph of Arimathea offered the burial place he had prepared for himself, which was located near the crucifixion site, for Jesus' burial. According to Christian belief, three days later the tomb was found empty—Jesus was resurrected from the dead. "You see," said Jamie, "Jesus rose from the dead. How else do you explain the empty tomb?"

"Those who do not accept the Christian belief suggest that what really happened was there was no time on Friday afternoon before sundown and the onset of the Sabbath to find a burial site for Jesus, so he was buried temporarily in Joseph's prepared tomb. On Sunday, after the Sabbath, he was taken by the three Marys to an empty tomb on Mount of Olives and buried there in a permanent site."

"Heresy, my friend," countered Jamie. "Absolute heresy."

"Tolerance, my friend," I said. "Absolute tolerance."

יְהוָה

Hundreds of people were waiting in line to dip their fingers in the holy oil from the lamps around the grotto and rub it on their hands and legs.

"Why are they doing that?" asked Jamie in awe, but also with a note of cynicism.

"They believe it has special healing powers," I explained. "To you and me it may seem foolish and superstitious, but to them it is real and holy. Besides, is it really very different from the way we saw Jews believing that blue stones at the base of their home will keep away the evil eye and protect them from illness and tragedy? Or even your Protestant belief that faith alone will save you from damnation and hell?

"Remember, Jamie, for us Jews your faith seems no less unreasonable than those people over there who believe in the healing power of that oil. Remember also that the real test of your newfound born-again faith is whether you can combine it with tolerance and respect for those who differ. Commitment with tolerance, that's the formula for faith-full living."

"Well said," Jamie replied. "I'm telling you, you should have been a preacher. You missed your calling. But it's never too late!" he added with a smile.

We watched the people patiently wait in line and rub the lamp's oil on themselves. I stood in awe at the sincerity of their belief, the purity of their heart, and their yearning hope for physical healing.

"I envy the simplicity of their faith," I said, "the uncomplicated, nondialectical nature of their faith. They seem to accept God's existence and healing power without questioning or doubt and with absolute certainty in God's deliverance. This sense of the numinous, or what Rudolf Otto calls the *mysterium tremendum,* is really at the core of all faiths and of faith itself. There's something beautiful and admirable about such faith. Frankly, I envy it. But for whatever reason—and it's probably the confluence of many factors—my faith is more complex and often lacks that sense of absolute trust, pure certainty, and utter simplicity."

יְהוָה

We walked to Mount Zion and visited the Upper Room, one of the most important sites for evangelical Protestants. According to the New Testament, fifty days after Passover began and Jesus was crucified, on the holiday of Pentecost or *Shavuot* in Hebrew, one hundred and twenty of Jesus' followers gathered in that room where they were sanctified by the Holy Spirit. This is what led them to speak in tongues and commit themselves to carrying the message of Christianity to the four corners of the world.

A group of Christians from Denmark were with us in the Upper Room, soulfully singing the beautiful praise chorus "Hallelujah." I am always deeply moved by the power of that song. And though I am not a Christian, the words are most meaningful—and theologically kosher—to me, as well. As we left the Upper Room, I pointed out to Jamie the biblical Hebrew verse on the sign on the wall of the yeshiva next door, and translated it for him: *For my house shall be the house for all the nations.*

יְהוָה

After a brief stop for a bite of lunch, we walked to an important site for Catholics and Protestants alike—Peter Ingalitantra, where Peter denied three times before the cock crowed that he was a follower of Jesus. Actually, this was the home of Caiaphas, the wealthy son of the high priest.

When Caiaphas became high priest, he made his basement, which was a stable, into a prison and his cistern of water into a dungeon. According to tradition, this is where Jesus was brought to spend the night before being taken by Pilot's guards to the northern portion of the city. And it was here that a local resident recognized Peter as a Galilean as he was sitting on the steps to see what would happen to Jesus. It was here where he denied his master, Jesus.

We walked down the narrow stone steps, descending deeper and deeper into history. We descended all the way down to the basement level, into a dark and dreary dungeon. I was uncomfortable yet curious about the place. But as I looked over at Jamie, he was swooning, about to pass out.

"I can't breathe," he said to me, grabbing my arm. "I feel like I'm going to faint."

"Hang in there, buddy," I said, putting his arm around my shoulder and helping him up the stairs.

"Thanks," he said as we reached the ground level and walked out into the yard. "I felt like I did a few days ago at Yad Vashem. Remember when we walked through the children's memorial? I felt the same way—holding on to the rail, grappling insecurely for my footing in the dark, gasping for air. The thought that Jesus walked down those very stairs and spent the night in that dungeon, being mocked by the soldiers and knowing fully well he was going to die the next day... and that he did it all for me, so I might have eternal life. Do you remember John 3:16? 'God so loved the world that he gave his only Son, so that everyone who believes in him may not perish but may have eternal life.' That's what I felt down there. Jesus' suffering."

"But also your redemption," I added.

"Indeed, Yechiel. But once again, I fail to understand God's logic in bringing you into the picture and having you, a Jew, facilitate my salvation. And now you carried me in your arms and helped me out of the dungeon. You figuratively and physically raised me from the depths of despair and sin. Rabbi, I will forever be grateful to you."

"Just goes to show you," I responded, "God has a sense of humor. And besides, why does it come as such a shock that I, a Jew, helped you in your return home to your spiritual center? After all, Jesus, your lord, was from my tribe. He *was* a Jew, you know."

"Anyhow," said Jamie, "thanks, my friend. Rest assured I won't disappoint you with my articles."

What more could I have wanted from our journey together? A good series of features on Israel, a soul redeemed, and a new friend. This was the first time Jamie actually called me friend, and it came *after* he became a Christian and renewed his faith convictions.

"How authentic are these holy sites?" asked Jamie as we stepped into our still intact rental car.

"Some, very clearly, are," I responded, "though others are based more on embellished tradition than historical fact. On the other hand, I've come to respect the validity of those traditions. For if Christians and Jews were willing to die to preserve these sites, as they have for centuries, and to maintain the traditions associated with them through the generations, that is itself a serious indication of their authenticity. And even if they turn out to be, in fact, inauthentic, they certainly serve a positive role by inspiring believers to greater spiritual heights. Or must I remind you of what happened to you a few minutes ago?"

יְהֹוָה

We drove past *Givat Hatachmoshet*, the hill that served as the key Jordanian bunker guarding entry into the old city during the 1967 War. For some reason, it has always been an important place for me, even a holy site, not because of any biblical significance, but because of the spirit of those Jews who died there. It was essential for Israel to conquer this ridge in 1967, since it opened the way to Mount Scopus. From there, the army was able to go south to the Mount of Olives, and from there to the Lions' Gate, and from there into the Old City and Kotel. It was the valor and martyrdom of those Jews who died in the fierce battle that enabled Jamie and me to pray at the Kotel and visit the Old City together.

We walked through the complex maze of trenches surrounding the bunker, and I imagined what the battle was like. There was an Israeli tank on the field, kept there as a relic from the war. I watched the children playing on it and wondered, could this be a modern day idiom portending the day prophesied long ago, when men would turn their swords into plowshares? When one nation would not lift up sword against another nation and neither would learn war any more? When people would rest securely under their tree and no one would be afraid? When God would wipe the tears of suffering from mankind's face?

The sun was setting as we made our way to the car. We saw a group of Hassidic Jews getting out of their car, standing on the side of the road, and davening mincha, the afternoon prayers that must be recited before sundown. Just a few yards away was a group of Muslims prostrating themselves in prayer too. The two groups gazed at each other with mistrust and fear.

"I'll bet those people don't realize they're really cousins, family, praying to the same God. "I prayed that these two peoples—Moslems and Jews—will yet discover that though they face different directions in prayer—Moslems toward Mecca and Jews toward Jerusalem—they pray together, albeit separately, to the same heavenly God who loves them both.

"The two are better off than one," says the Bible, and "a three-fold cord is not readily broken." Christians, Moslems, and Jews, a threefold cord.

The world sometimes appears to me to be in its forty-ninth level of impurity. I pray the mashiach will come and bring healing and shalom among us speedily in our day before, God forbid, it is too late.

We walked over to the Garden Tomb, which Protestants believe to be Calvary. (See John 19:40-42.) Today it is located in a bustling Arab portion of the city. It is also believed to be the northernmost point of Mount Moriah where Abraham was commanded to sacrifice his son, Isaac. It is believed that Jeremiah was imprisoned there too. According to the book of Hebrews, Jesus was brought here after having been spat upon and judged.

Across the street, underneath the Damascus Gate, an arch still remains from the old northern gate of the ancient city of Jerusalem. Protestants believe that Jesus was brought through that gate to this site of Golgotha, where he was crucified outside the city walls as Roman law dictated.

"If you look at the shape of the rocks of this mountain," I pointed out to Jamie, "you can discern two eye sockets and a nose looking like a skull. Perhaps this really was the site of Calvary."

A group of British tourists were taking Communion at the Garden Tomb, and I realized this was *their* Western Wall. Discovered just one hundred years ago, this Protestant holy site competes for authenticity with the Catholic Church's Holy Sepulchre, whose origins date back to the fourth century. I wondered why Protestants and Catholics must be so divided about this, and why they can't get along with one another. Then I thought of northern Ireland, and the Middle East and Rwanda, even Los Angeles, and was pained by all the discord and fratricide in the world.

I watched the people deep in solemn prayer, and was moved by the spirit of holiness permeating the air. They began to sing. I thought how different their spirituality was experienced and expressed from that of the Hassidim we visited just a few days earlier, and yet how similar their attachment to God and their feeling of his holy presence in that moment.

Perhaps the Mahayana Buddhists were right. Perhaps religion is but the raft that enables us to cross the river of life and reach the other side. Judaism is my raft; Christianity is Jamie's. And we ought not confuse the raft with the other side. We dare not absolutize the raft and imbue it with exclusive truth. To do so is idolatry, which, like Paul Tillich, I understand as misplaced ultimacy.

As we left the Garden Tomb, we saw a sign with Romans 1:4 written on it: JESUS CHRIST DECLARED WITH POWER TO BE THE SON OF GOD BY HIS RESURRECTION FROM THE DEAD. A Jewish man passing by saw me coming out with my yarmulke, and he turned away indignantly, no doubt assuming I am a Jew for Jesus. While I still don't believe in Jesus as the Christ as Jamie does, and view him instead as a Jew who brought salvation to the gentiles, in some respects, that is exactly what I have become... a Jew for Jesus.

"There's even greater evidence this is Golgotha," I added. "According to the New Testament, Joseph had a tomb covered by a rolling stone in his garden. Around a hundred years ago, a Jewish grave or sepulcher with such a stone was found right near here."

We walked over to the tomb and stepped inside. Could these walls have held the body of Jesus?

"Ultimately," I said, "we'll never know with certainty what is historically true and what is not. But it's important to look beyond the physical site itself to the deeper spiritual meaning it embodies, to our hearts' yearning for the living

God. So, I say, if these holy sites help Christians come closer to their lord, and Jews closer to theirs, they have achieved their divine objective."

"It's just so amazing to believe," whispered Jamie, "that this is where it all happened. Right here in the places we visited today. This whole day brought me closer to my Lord and to my faith. For the first time, the Bible has come alive for me as a reality. To think that it was right here in Jerusalem that my Lord Jesus was brought to the house of Pontius Pilot, judged, stripped of his clothing, humiliated, and hung on the cross. I still can't get over it. Right here, where I am standing, Jesus likely stood. Right here is where the events that changed the entire world and course of history, the lives of billions of people, took place. Just mind-boggling."

"Awesome," I responded, mimicking my teenage kids—and Jamie.

As we looked out on the thousands of Christian pilgrims visiting their holy sites and retracing the life of Jesus, I said, "You know, Jamie, you're not going to like what I say, but I now feel comfortable enough with you to say it. The fact is, I often feel I have a deeper understanding of Jesus of Nazareth—who he was and what his life was like—than all those pilgrims out there recovering the Jewish roots of their faith and background of their lord, Jesus."

"I never would have understood that before," replied Jamie, "and it would have sounded like real chutzpa, too. But now I understand."

"The fact is," I continued, "Jesus was not a Christian like they think, but a Jew like me who practiced Judaism and went to synagogue and probably ate kosher, too. But permit me to go even further, and please don't take offense. From a Jewish perspective, Jesus was one of hundreds, if not thousands, of Jews crucified by the Romans, though his death certainly changed history as no other Jew's did.

"For through him, generations of people were taught to accept our *Torah* and the one true God. Through Jesus, multitudes of nations were grafted onto the olive tree of Israel and into relationship with God."

"If you can't accept Jesus for yourself," interrupted Jamie, "can you accept that this is 'of the Lord'? That he was sent by God to bring salvation to the world? You Jews are always talking of being a light unto nations, and of sharing your spiritual treasure with the world. Well, maybe Jesus was one of the ways in which God orchestrated this whole drama so that through you 'all the nations of the world will be blessed.'"

"You're raising some penetrating questions, Jamie. After all, who can comprehend the mystery of God's ways? For as the prophet reminds us, God's ways are not man's, and his thoughts are not ours."

"Maybe we need to look at this the way Rabbi Gamaliel did in the book of Acts," said Jamie, "with a wait-and-see attitude. If it lasts and bears fruit, it is 'of the Lord.'"

"That's an acceptable Jewish view and is even cited in the Ethics of the Fathers, which states that a disagreement which is authentic and 'for the sake of heaven' can be determined by whether it stands the test of time."

Jamie pressed the limits further. "You don't accept that Jesus was resurrected, but you can accept the possibility that he was buried temporarily in Joseph's borrowed tomb and reburied three days later in a different permanent resting place. That being the case, can you accept that God orchestrated the scenario in such a way as to enable Jesus' followers to believe he was miraculously and supernaturally resurrected? So billions of gentiles would come to believe in Jesus' divinity and resurrection and come to know the God of Israel? Put differently, is it possible, from a Jewish perspective, that Jesus was, in some way, sent by God to bring salvation to the gentiles?"

I had never before been confronted by this argument, and it seemed eminently reasonable to me. "Yes," I said, "I believe it is definitely possible that Jesus the Jew was in some way sent by God to bring salvation to the gentiles and redemption to the world." I was shocked by what I had just said, but at peace with it. As radical as it seemed, I believed it was right. And even great Rabbis Maimonedes and Meiri, I remembered, shared a similar view.

Jamie smiled broadly and said, "Okay, you're almost there!"

"Don't push it," I responded, smiling too. Funny, I did not feel at all threatened by this new belief.

"Well then," said Jamie, "it's time you Jews proudly reclaimed Jesus as one of your own. I don't recall ever hearing a Jew say something like, 'look at what the Romans did to our Jesus,' though you certainly acknowledge the martyrdom of other Jews over the centuries."

"You're right," I said. "I admit you have a point. On the other hand, maybe you Christians drove us away from that acknowledgment by constantly saying 'look at what you Jews did by crucifying our Lord Jesus' and persecuting us for it—as if we killed him or that he wasn't one of our own."

"You have a point too, I admit it," Jamie said. "Maybe it's time that Jesus' Jewishness, which was denied by both communities for so many centuries and buried in history under the rubble of polemic, was reclaimed by both communities."

"That'll take a lot of mutual trust, dialogue, and goodwill." I said.

"Indeed. It gives us something to strive toward," Jamie replied.

Making our way back to the car, we saw an Arab carrying a box of turtledoves to sell in the market.

"You don't see that too often in Chicago," said Jamie. "Reminds me of the Song of Solomon."

"I'm told they stuff the birds with rice, and then cook and eat them," I said.

The neighborhood in which the Garden Tomb is located is an Arab one. Immediately adjacent to it, is the *Meah Shearim*. In the course of the week, we had visited these three faith communities, living within yards of one another, with little or no contact, understanding, and tolerance toward one another. I looked at the faces of the Arab women peeking out from behind the black scarves covering their heads. Some of them seemed so young, with children of their own. I wondered, are these not regular people like me, seeking to lead a normal life, to raise children, take a vacation, and retire in good health and dignity? I wondered anew why Moslems, Christians, and Jews can't get along with one another, and even among themselves. Is this factionalism, ultimately, the destiny of the people here? Can the walls of separation and discord ever be breached? Do good fences in the city of Jerusalem really make good neighbors? And then I stood in awe at what God was able to do in bonding Jamie and me, and I was left with hope.

CHAPTER THIRTEEN
THE JOURNEY HOME

It was Friday afternoon, and Jamie and I shifted over to Tel Aviv to be near Ben Gurion International Airport. Tomorrow night we would return home to our family, friends, and daily routine. Jamie would will take all his notes and write the feature articles he was sent to do. We had come a long way in the past few days, and had met with results I never anticipated. Jamie had been strengthened as a Christian and I as a Jew. Moreover, our bonds with one another, with each other's faith, and with this special land that had been the focus of our attention and source of our personal inspiration and growth, had been deeply strengthened and enriched. It was a surprisingly great trip. And yet, I remained unsettled, tense, and distraught.

יהוה

As often as I visit Israel, and as deeply attached as I become to her each time, I cannot escape the most fundamental inner contradiction of my life. I am a proud American Jew who is deeply appreciative of the freedoms and blessings I enjoy but who remains, ultimately, incomplete outside the land of Israel. My life's spiritual journey—and emotional equilibrium—seems to forever oscillate between highs and lows, ups and downs, depending on whether or not I am here. I never seem to be able to reach and maintain the state that the Buddhists so beautifully refer to as *nirvana*.

I still remember my sadness, after reading *Siddhartha* in high school and asking my teacher whether we ever reach the state of enlightenment that Siddhartha did, or if it forever eludes us. I'll never forget her answer. "Don't expect to find unbridled joy and comfort and peace in life. The message of *Siddhartha* is that life is suffering; we never arrive at the Promised Land. It is the spiritual journey and search that must bring you fulfillment and satisfaction."

I remember responding—rather brazenly, looking back at it now—that I didn't mind the journey if the prize at the end was both worthwhile *and* attainable. But I couldn't see myself struggling all my life for a goal I could not reach, and giving ultimacy to the search itself. After all, Moses' predicament in seeing the Promised Land from afar but not entering it was a curse.

My problem, as best I understood it, was that I was worshiping two masters and that I had two loves, America and Israel. I was happy, comfortable, and, on one level, fulfilled in the U.S. It was my home, after all. Yet I desperately wanted to be one with my people, my nation, my God, and, most of all, with my self.

יהוה

Jamie sensed the stirrings of my heart—my emotional anxiety, fears, and sense of dislocation. "It must be hard for you to return to America after being here," he said. "I'm sorry my visit disturbed your equanimity."

"More than you'll ever know," I said.

He looked into my eyes and, much like the Rebbe had done a few days earlier, seemed to see through to my soul. I felt like a pressure cooker ready to explode, needing release and closure, not doubt and ambiguity. I was reminded of Elijah in his confrontation with the idol worshipers of Baal on Mount Carmel. "How long will you teeter on both sides of the fence—if to Baal, so be it. And if to God, to God." I knew I had to make a choice—to return to my home in Chicago or remain in my homeland in Israel. I could no longer bear the tension and contradiction of my life, living contentedly in the U.S. but feeling spiritually bereft there. It was tearing me apart.

"How long do you think you can defer making the big decision?" said Jamie, reading my mind and seeming to know exactly what I was struggling with.

I gazed into his soft eyes, which were filled with compassion, and understanding and revealed to him my soul:

"I don't know, Jamie. I just don't know."

"Let's go for a walk before we pack up," said Jamie, changing the subject and trying to defuse the tension.

"Good idea," I responded.

We walked for close to an hour, mostly in silence, on the beautiful shores of Tel Aviv beach. The boardwalk was filled with Israelis and tourists enjoying the *Shabbat* atmosphere.

"What's going on over there?" asked Jamie, pointing to one of the beachfront hotels.

A crowd had gathered around a group of about twenty Israelis who were dancing variations of the *hora* to the strains of Israeli folk music. It was the kind of scene I remembered seeing in old film clips of Israeli life in the kibbutz, and of the spontaneous joy that broke out into song and dance on May 14, 1948, when the United Nations voted to grant Israel statehood.

We waded into the crowd as the song changed to a traditional Yemenite tune. There was something very pure and authentic about these people, something even holy about them, even though they were secular Jews clearly violating Jewish law, which prohibits the playing of music on *Shabbat*. Most of these people had probably served in the Israeli army, fought in one or more of its wars, and lost either a family member or friend in battle. They were Jews, young and old, from different backgrounds and cultures, whose families had emigrated to Israel from Russia, Yemen, Tunisia, Germany, Ethiopia, the United States, and dozens of other countries. Some were dancing and singing, many with little children in their arms; others were standing around watching, like me. Most of these people probably came here under duress—as survivors of the Holocaust, refugees from Arab lands, or escapees from anti-Semitism in their host nations. Their decision to emigrate to Israel was less a matter of choice than one of necessity. But these people had come together and cast their destiny with one another.

I felt at one with them, no less than I did with the ultra Orthodox Hassidic Jews I was with at the tisch a few days ago. These were my people, and I was suddenly filled with a tremendous love for them and all Jews here. I realized that my existential emptiness and anxiety stemmed from the fact that I felt apart from them. I had not cast my life and future destiny with my people. A verse from scripture kept coming to my mind, "I will abide among the children of Israel."

Jamie and I listened to the music and watched the people dance. These weren't professional dancers, just regular Israelis out enjoying themselves on a *Shabbat* afternoon. The deejay put on an old Israeli song I had not heard for you to return to America after being here," he said. "I'm sorry my visit disturbed your equanimity."

"More than you'll ever know," I said.

He looked into my eyes and, much like the Rebbe had done a few days earlier, seemed to see through to my soul. I felt like a pressure cooker ready to explode, needing release and closure, not doubt and ambiguity. I was reminded of Elijah in his confrontation with the idol worshipers of Baal on Mount Carmel. "How long will you teeter on both sides of the fence—if to Baal, so be it. And if to God, to God." I knew I had to make a choice—to return to my home in Chicago or remain in my homeland in Israel. I could no longer bear the tension and contradiction of my life, living contentedly in the U.S. but feeling spiritually bereft there. It was tearing me apart.

"How long do you think you can defer making the big decision?" said Jamie, reading my mind and seeming to know exactly what I was struggling with.

I gazed into his soft eyes, which were filled with compassion, and understanding and revealed to him my soul:

"I don't know, Jamie. I just don't know."

"Let's go for a walk before we pack up," said Jamie, changing the subject and trying to defuse the tension.

"Good idea," I responded.

We walked for close to an hour, mostly in silence, on the beautiful shores of Tel Aviv beach. The boardwalk was filled with Israelis and tourists enjoying the *Shabbat* atmosphere.

"What's going on over there?" asked Jamie, pointing to one of the beachfront hotels.

A crowd had gathered around a group of about twenty Israelis who were dancing variations of the *hora* to the strains of Israeli folk music. It was the kind of scene I remembered seeing in old film clips of Israeli life in the kibbutz, and of the spontaneous joy that broke out into song and dance on May 14, 1948, when the United Nations voted to grant Israel statehood.

We waded into the crowd as the song changed to a traditional Yemenite tune. There was something very pure and authentic about these people, something even holy about them, even though they were secular Jews clearly violating Jewish law, which prohibits the playing of music on *Shabbat*. Most of these people had probably served in the Israeli army, fought in one or more of its wars, and lost either a family member or friend in battle. They were Jews, young and old, from different backgrounds and cultures, whose families had emigrated to Israel from Russia, Yemen, Tunisia, Germany, Ethiopia, the United States, and dozens of other countries. Some were dancing and singing, many with little children in their arms; others were standing around watching, like me. Most of these people probably came here under duress—as survivors of the Holocaust, refugees from Arab lands, or escapees from anti-Semitism in their host nations. Their decision to emigrate to Israel was less a matter of choice than one of necessity. But these people had come together and cast their destiny with one another.

I felt at one with them, no less than I did with the ultra Orthodox Hassidic Jews I was with at the tisch a few days ago. These were my people, and I was suddenly filled with a tremendous love for them and all Jews here. I realized that my existential emptiness and anxiety stemmed from the fact that I felt apart from them. I had not cast my life and future destiny with my people. A verse from scripture kept coming to my mind, "I will abide among the children of Israel."

Jamie and I listened to the music and watched the people dance. These weren't professional dancers, just regular Israelis out enjoying themselves on a *Shabbat* afternoon. The deejay put on an old Israeli song I had not heard for years, "Arava," describing the pioneering work cultivating the Negev Desert.

I could not hold myself back any longer. I began weeping uncontrollably. At that moment, I felt clarity of life—purpose that I never knew before, a bolt of lightning that illuminated my entire ethos. It became clear to me, as clear as day. This is where I wanted to live out my life—in this place and among this people. This is where I felt truly complete and at home, alive and holy, where my life has meaning and purpose. I don't know what I can bring to this country. But I know what it can bring to me—spiritual fulfillment. *Siddhartha* was wrong. One *can* arrive at his destination; the journey is not the ultimate goal. In that instant, I knew I had to "choose life," as the Bible says.

There exists for every person a resting place, like that which Noah's raven found, a place in life and time and space where, after a lifetime of coping with spiritual journeying, inner contradictions, and struggle for fulfillment, one arrives. That place was right in front of my eyes and heart all along. But I have to choose it as my own, take upon myself what Kierkegaard called a *leap of faith* and put aside the complexities and challenges that obscure the clarity of vision. It is, after all is said and done, my life and my own unique soul.

In that split instant, I realized my life struggle was finally over; the soft inner voice that I had tried to suppress for so long now became a clarion call that I could no longer ignore—and I surrendered to it. A smile came over my face, and a warm feeling, of shalom, peace, God's peace, enveloped my heart. My life burden was lifted, much like Jamie's had been the day before when he made his decision to surrender his struggle and commit his life to Christ. We both had our born-again experience, and our experiences would forever transform our lives.

"I know that smile," said Jamie. "Looks like you've been touched by an epiphany."

I looked over at Jamie, the Baptist journalist I had just met a few days ago. I wondered why God would reveal himself so powerfully to me and point the way home for me through this trip with a Christian. The lord, indeed, works in mysterious ways. And he has a keen sense of humor, too.

Seeing me feel woozy and struggling to maintain my balance, Jamie put his arm around me and held me up. Smiling, he turned to me and said: "Good for you, my new Israeli-American friend. *Kol hakavod.*"